From
Nothing
to
Nursing

How to Become an
RN in the US

by Nurse Help Desk

Dedication

For all the nurses that show up every day. For the preceptors, charge nurses and co-workers who made me into a nurse. Special thanks to Kelly, who turned me into an L&D nurse and then helped deliver my son. Lastly, thank you to my Mom, my husband, Cara and Aleisha, my biggest nursing cheerleaders.

TABLE OF CONTENTS

PART III: YOUR FIRST RN JOB

Introduction

Welcome! I am so happy you are reading this guide. I wrote it originally for a friend who was considering nursing as a career but felt lost. I empathized with her struggle. I had found the process of becoming a nurse daunting and at times I had no clue where to look for answers to my questions. I started writing things out for her and I sent it along piecemeal. She asked me if she could share it with others. After about six months I had given her about 50 pages of advice to which she replied, "this needs to be a book.

It's here now for your use as a guide towards a successful career as an RN. It will take you through the stages of becoming a nurse. Part I is meant for someone who is a pre-nursing student or someone who's considering a career in nursing. Part II is for those starting or currently in nursing school. Part III is for getting your first RN job and possibly your dream job.

My experience is within the routes and culture of nursing in the US, and so all of the text pertains to how nursing is in the US. Also, this is based on my experience, in one state, at a handful of schools and hospitals. Not every sentence will apply to every reader depending on your location and school or hospital policies and culture. I welcome collaboration and suggestions about the pursuit of nursing as a career in other states and countries.

I recommend starting the guidebook by reading for the stage you are at. You might not want to jump to Part III, for example, until you have a grip on what kind of nursing program you want to attend. It's easy to get overwhelmed. Just take on one step at a time, one class at a time, and you'll get there.

Nursing is one of the many professions where you can't understand what it's actually like until you are in it. For this reason, it's in your best interest to absorb as many sources of positive and negative information of what it's like to work as an RN to get as much insight as possible to see if it's for you. There are multiple further reading suggestions in the text and at nursehelpdesk.com if you wish to learn more.

The goal here is for you to find your route to becoming a working RN no matter where you are in the journey. If I have saved you a few hours of research or stress then I have done my job with this guide. I am genuinely happy you are here and want you to know how to make it as a new nurse. We need you!

Please reach out with any questions or feedback at nursehelpdesk.com.

PART I

THE PRE-NURSING STUDENT

Part I is for someone who is considering a career in nursing and is curious about school paths and options. There is reinforcement and good-to-knows if you have already decided to start the route to become a nursing student.

CHAPTER ONE

SHOULD YOU BECOME A NURSE?

There are so many reasons why someone would choose to become a nurse. Wanting to help people, a solid, steady career, plus generally good health, and retirement benefits are all valid reasons to be interested in this career. I became a nurse because I always had an interest in it, it seemed like a solid way to earn a living, and I liked the idea of being present for the intense moments of people's lives and helping in some way. It felt like "real life," if that makes sense. I also love working with patients from all walks of life that I otherwise might not have the chance to be around. Below are some more pros and many cons of nursing.

Some Pros of Becoming a Nurse

There are various areas of focus and types of people to care for. From routine healthy people to very sick patients, to accidents and trauma, to births, surgery, to caring for newborns and kids, to clerical, research, and teaching, there is a lot of variety possible in a nursing career.

A science degree all by itself (which is what you earn to become a nurse) will likely raise your intelligence level and make you an overall smarter person.

Nurses work in hospitals and clinics. They work on ambulances, at theme parks and schools, in offices, labs and from home. There are a wide variety of settings and environments.

There's a lot of respect in the profession. Generally speaking, when someone hears that you are a nurse, it is often well-received. Often, landlords love renting to nurses, banks like lending to nurses, etc. Especially now, it's well thought of and trusted profession.

There are flexible options for working. This includes 12-hour shifts, 8-hour shifts, 10-hour shifts, or other variations of part-time, full time, per diem, day shift, evening shift, night shift. It's also conducive to having a lot of time off compared to other professions depending on what you choose. For example, you work three 12 hour shifts a week, you get four full days off every week.

Because of this, there are a lot of opportunities to pick up extra work, overtime, take a second job, etc., if that's of interest to you.

As an RN, if not in management, you do your work, you clock out, and you're done. You do your hours, work your shifts; unpaid extra work at home is not required. You're off time is your own, and very rarely are you required to do work outside of your scheduled hours. Overtime is excellent, holiday pay is excellent, etc. For every minute you work extra, you are paid for it vs. a salary position where that is not the case.

You may get more time off to travel vs. other careers. Many nurses arrange their schedules to be able to travel a lot. i.e., one week they work Sunday-Tuesday and the next week Thursday-Saturday. Meaning they have 8 days off in between! You can go on a trip without taking any work time off.

Calling out sick as a floor RN means that someone with your exact skill set will take your place that day, unlike other careers where the work you didn't get done while you were out ill is waiting for you when you get back. Same in the case of vacation, you don't need to do double work before or after your time off to make up for the days you weren't there.

There are opportunities to advance and ascend to management roles.

Usually, working for a hospital comes with generous health care and benefits for you and your family. Often there are retirement options as well.

Your work involves other people, talking to them, caring for them.

You have the chance to make a positive impact in someone's life. If you're good, it's likely your patient will remember you. Many say that nursing has given them a fulfilling and meaningful career.

You get to care for all types of folks from all walks of life that you otherwise might not have frequent opportunities to interact with.

You gain a lot of knowledge about life, the human body, illness, and disease. This can be empowering if something happens to your own health or those around you. It means a lot to me to be able to be a knowledgeable ear for a friend or family member that is dealing with something heavy.

There are a lot of protections as an employee if you are part of a union, and a lot is negotiated for you. Pay increases, safe patient ratios, mandatory breaks are all perks of being in a union.

You have the easiest workwear. Typically you wear scrubs which are kind of like wearing pajamas. You are expected to be clean and professional looking as a nurse, but you are not expected to be super made up; it's your choice. You wear comfortable shoes.

It's a physically active job; you are often on your feet and walking most of your day.

As of now, it's an incredibly stable job. Once you are experienced, it's likely you will always be able to find work no matter where you are.

Your performance is not based on your age or your looks; you are judged by your work.

You can expect financial independence. You won't be rolling in money, but even in the most expensive cities, you will make enough to have some kind of roof over your head, probably even a nice one. Most of the nurses I know own their homes, drive well-running cars, help their families, take vacations, etc.

Once you are assimilated into a particular department, you can form really special bonds with your co-workers. You'll go through stressful experiences with other nurses and staff. When you come out the other side, you will have a bond. Those bonds are pretty strong and can result in long-lasting friendships and make work much more fun.

Some Cons of Becoming a Nurse

You will see people at their absolute worst, some who have made really bad choices. This will possibly cloud your judgment of people and humanity in general. Watching a mom who received zero prenatal care deliver a baby while high on meth and then walk out the next day without caring about her child is disheartening. Seeing someone shot or beaten in the ER. Someone losing their cool over their health blaming you and doctors when it was their actions that got them there.

While you will likely get used to it, you will see lots of blood, vomit, feces, urine. Someone might even try to throw it at you at some point. Hopefully not.

You might see dead bodies. You may try to bring them back to life, and at times, it won't work. In pediatrics and the ER, you might see children who have died or are dying. In L&D, you could see moms or babies who are dying or have died. You also will be in the presence of unimaginable grief, and you still have to do your job.

You will put yourself in potentially harmful scenarios with patients that have diseases, and contagious illnesses. There might be angry, possibly violent patients and family. There are of course, protections in place, but accidents still happen, and you could potentially become injured or infected.

You will encounter patients who are doing severe harm to themselves, their families and their children, and sometimes unborn babies. You only get a short time with them, and it's unlikely you can do anything about it. This can overall be very depressing, and you may become cynical as a result.

Depending on your job, it's likely to be in many ways high stress and/or requiring a lot of nonstop work. It's common to be unable to sit down except for breaks for an entire shift.

There are difficult patients who, for either mental health reasons or personality reasons, are not willing to comply with their plan of care. You have to figure out how to serve care to these people. For example, there are patients with dementia that no matter how many times you tell them not to get out of bed without calling you, will still try to get out of bed. When they do and fall, it's on you and a big problem.

Sometimes there are difficult families. There will be a family member who will try to film everything that you do (you can tell them to stop, they have no right to film you), there will be family members who question everything you do, there will be family members who constantly ask you for things and accuse you of doing the wrong thing or not enough. They often have very high expectations of how their loved ones should be cared for. We should always try to exceed expectations of care, but it can be exhausting to keep up with a demanding family member while also completing all of the tasks needed to care for the patient while being mindful of regulations and rules of the hospital.

Long hours of a shift can be too much for some. The job is physically exhausting, no matter how in shape you are. It's also mentally exhausting in many ways. You deal with and field other's emotions, and it can affect you greatly.

Taking care of others and being a front-line caregiver requires a high responsibility level and, in turn, can yield high stress all day until you clock out. A lot is expected of you, and you have to provide a high standard of care at all times. You are expected to be nice and respectful to a patient at all times, even when you don't want to.

Going to and getting through nursing school takes up a lot of attention. You likely will have a more rigorous college experience and won't be able to have as much downtime as other majors. While you may have time for family or significant other, other hobbies and interests will be pushed to the back burner. You potentially could lose friends, not being able to show up for them the way you did before.

You field a lot of negative human emotion every day and if you are a sensitive person or are unable to sort out a way to cope, your emotional state could be worsened. The negative emotions of patients, families, doctors, etc. are often passed through you and you have to deal with every person and issue in a professional way all day long.

There can be a steep and stressful learning curve out of school, and it can be very hard for some (author included) to bridge from New Grad RN to a functioning floor nurse.

Like in many work environments, there can be bullies. Whether doctors, co-workers or leaders, it's often a part of the profession.

It is very hard to work if you aren't feeling well and you have to try to be mentally sharp. Being a hungover nurse is not responsible. Showing up to work ill is also not ok.

Do you have to Care about People to Become a Nurse?

Yes, you do. We are working on the assumption that you want to help people in your future profession and that you are considering nursing as a way to do this. It also helps to have some inherent qualities such as empathy and compassion for others. This is something that I see in most successful nurses at their core. This book will not teach you how to have compassion and empathy for others, we are assuming that you already have this even if in small amounts. If you do not, this is probably not the profession for you.

For further reading on caring as a nurse I recommend *Nursing: The Philosophy and Science of Caring* by Jean Watson. She is a nursing theorist and goes into excellent detail about what it means to care for others.

Recommended Ways to See if Nursing is for You:

Try to work in a hospital in a role with patient interaction. You can get trained fairly quickly to become a Certified Nurse Assistant (CNA). Another option is to work as an Emergency Medical Technician (1-2 semesters of training). Another option might be as a transporter in a hospital. Administrative personnel within a hospital can be an option as well, like as a Unit Secretary. Working as a Scrub Tech requires quite a bit of school, and these jobs are very competitive in many areas. Becoming a Medical Assistant is another idea, and MA's most often work in a clinic setting.

Try to volunteer in a hospital. Hospitals have extensive volunteer programs, and some are competitive. If you go this route, you'll have to make your own luck in what you'll get to see when you are volunteering by being proactive with helping the staff that you are with. See the chapter on making the most of your nursing school clinicals to learn some tips on this.

Is there a health care professional that you know that you could shadow or talk to? This can take some work on your part; signing hospital releases, coordinating schedules, but you potentially could see some good stuff.

Ask yourself if you are tolerant of "gross" stuff? Or do you think you can get over it? You'll see a lot, and you'll see people at their absolute worst.

14

We're talking vomit, feces, urine, and actual dead people sometimes. You will see a lot of body parts too. I used to have a hard time watching someone throw up, now I am totally over it, but it took definite effort initially to not throw up myself.

Are you too old to become a nurse?

Nope, nope, nope.

I thought I was late in the game when I started on the road at 26. To my surprise, I was not even close to the oldest in my classes. I'd say I was about average age in my nursing program.

I work with several nurses now who got their RN license when they were 50. As long as you think you can physically do the job, totally go for it. And even if you don't think you can do a floor nurse job, there are other job options. But generally, know that you will be on your feet for many of the RN jobs out there. If you can handle it physically, there's no reason not to go for what you want.

Try not to worry about how long a goal will take. If it's something you want, you might as well go for it. The time will pass either way. Especially if you have 10+ working years left in you, you might as well have it be doing something you like and making good money for it.

How hard is it to become a nurse?

I'm sure there is someone out there who didn't have a hard time on the road to becoming a nurse. But everyone I have ever asked said that it ranged from very challenging to brutal. It takes several years of focused attention day in and day out, constantly focusing on your end goal. I'd say it's worth it if you want to do the work of being a nurse. If the work itself doesn't interest you, you might be disappointed when you are actually working as an RN.

Further Reading for more insight into what it's like being a nurse:

This Won't Hurt Me A Bit: What It's Really Like to Work in Healthcare by Josh McAdams

Oh Sh*t, I Almost Killed You! A Little Book of Big Things Nursing School Forgot to Teach You by Sonja Schwartzbach

CHAPTER TWO

NURSING SCHOOL PROGRAM OPTIONS

When I was first interested in pursuing nursing, I didn't know where to start. Hopefully, this will help you navigate your search bar in looking for schools, perusing college catalogs, and where to begin. Making an appointment with a college or high school counselor (if you are in high school) is also a great source of guidance for a particular school.

We will discuss nursing school prerequisite classes a lot in this chapter because it pertains to which programs you choose. But, we will dive into exactly what those classes are in Chapter 3.

Notes:

1. If your hope is to work in a hospital, your end goal should be to earn a Bachelor of Science in Nursing (BSN) or an MSN (Master's in Nursing). It is possible to work as an RN without a BSN degree, but hospitals prefer to hire BSN educated nurses. Or minimally RN's who are on their way to getting a BSN.

2. All of these routes require approximately 2-4 semesters of nursing school prerequisites plus being accepted into a specific school's nursing program and going through that nursing program. Expect a total of 6-10+ semesters/quarters.

Common Nursing Program Routes:

University Route

You attend a four-year private or public University or College (SF State or USF, for example) that has a nursing program (FYI: not all schools have nursing majors). Once you complete your pre-requisites or are very close to completing them, you apply and get accepted into your school's nursing program. Upon completion of that school's nursing program, you earn a Bachelor of Science in Nursing (BSN).

Pros:

- This is one of the most straightforward routes as you will only be dealing with one school.

- You can be certain that you are doing the exact right nursing pre-requisites (pre-reqs)that the school might require.

- There will likely be a smoother transition once you start nursing school because you already understand the administration and layout of the school.

- You will be on the school's radar already. Sometimes you get a slight preference when you apply over an outside candidate. Each school website will disclose that information.

- They may allow you to apply to their nursing program without all of the pre-reqs completed, and acceptance is contingent on getting certain grades. This allowance of overlap could result in little to no wait between pre-requisites and starting the nursing program.

Cons:

- This route can be very expensive.

- Sometimes university class schedules aren't always conducive to working a full-time job. Meaning, there are not many evening and weekend class options.

- If you only apply to that nursing program and don't get in, you have to either wait another year or choose a different major.

Cost:

Anywhere from $5,000 a semester to $20,000+ a semester for tuition.

Additional note:

Try very hard to get all of your general education degree requirements done before you start your actual nursing program. It's an unnecessary challenge to have to get through nursing school AND some random classes like history at the same time.

Timeline: 4-5 years

Extra remarks:

This is a common and, therefore, competitive route. Generally, excellent grades, volunteer work, being bilingual and other factors disclosed on a school's nursing website will help you get in.

Direct Entry Private or Public Nursing Universities:

Some schools will accept you into their nursing program before starting or completing your prerequisites. And as long as you pass the pre-reqs, you are guaranteed a spot in their nursing program. They offer BSN degrees mostly. These can be schools that specialize in only healthcare related degrees or regular universities that have many other majors. You can search for "direct entry nursing programs," to find these.

Pros:

- Start to finish 4-5 years with no wait to start in the nursing program after pre-reqs are completed.
- Pre-requisites and nursing program are at the same school.
- No further applications are required beyond initial applications, overall less stress for admittance.

Cons:

- Certain schools with this option, especially the cheaper ones, will likely be very difficult to get into.
- These schools *can* be very expensive, around $200,000+ for your degree program.
  Timeline: 4-5 years

Community College Route

Let's say you complete your nursing pre-reqs at a community college. Then you apply, are admitted into, and graduate from that community college's Nursing Program. You will earn an Associates' degree in Nursing (ADN) and be qualified to sit for NCLEX and become an RN.

Pros:

- High-quality education at a low cost.

- Nursing school pre-requisites at community colleges are often available on schedules conducive (if you can get in the class) for working individuals, i.e., nights or weekend classes.

- Many community college programs are well established as they were the first colleges in the U.S. to educate nurses.

- Usually, they have long-standing relationships with hospitals and have the same if not better clinical locations (practical education/training) as BSN students.

- Sometimes admittance to nursing programs at community colleges is lottery based, and you may have a better chance of getting into a nursing program by luck than by merit.

Cons:

- It can be difficult to get into pre-requisite classes as they have many more students wanting to take the classes than the seats available. Therefore, it can take longer to reach the goal. For the past 10-15 years, in many areas, the pre-requisite Science classes, in particular, are impacted.

- After graduating with ADN, it will take an additional 1-1.5 years to get a BSN degree.

- You could be limited to which hospitals will take you as a new grad without a BSN degree.
- It can be more challenging to get an RN job as you are potentially going for the same jobs as someone with a BSN.

Timeline: 3-6 semesters of pre-reqs and 4 semesters of RN classes = 4-5 years

Cost: Tuition is closer to $1,000 a semester, if not less.

Pre-Reqs at a Community College and then transferring into a University's Nursing Program

Example: Pre-reqs completed at City College of San Francisco and applying, being accepted to and graduating from SF State's Nursing program, and earning a BSN.

Pros:

Saving money the first two years of school by going to community college.

Cons:

This is a popular route, and transfer spots are competitive. An applicant could wait years before getting into a university nursing program even if well qualified.

Timeline: 2 years of school roughly for pre reqs, 2-2.5 years of school for BSN program. Total 4-5 years if no gaps.

Cost: roughly $1,000 a semester for community college (sometimes free depending on your income) and from $3,000-$20,000 a semester for a public or private university nursing program

Master's Level Entry Nursing Program (MEPN)

This is for those who have a Bachelors, Masters or higher in another subject.

For example, a person with a BFA gets nursing school prerequisites done at UC Berkeley extension. Then they apply and are accepted into UCSF's MEPN (Master's Entry Program for Nurses), graduate with a Master's in Nursing, and can get an RN license and now has an MSN degree.

Pros:

- These programs are sometimes accelerated, and so you gain a Master's and learn all of the nursing content in 2-3 years or so.
- MSN's are required to become a Nurse Practitioner and if that is a goal of yours, this is one way to do it.
- MEPN programs often are focused on research, an element required for Master's programs in many subjects.

Cons:

- Accelerated nursing programs usually mean very little time off, i.e., no Summer off.

- Programs are very intense from the start; there will be little room for much else in your life.

- MSN degrees are often more expensive than BSN degrees.

- These programs are very competitive and sometimes only have 20 or so spots with hundreds of applicants.

- Applicants must have very competitive pre-requisite grades and applications.

Timeline: 3 or so semesters of pre-requisites

(fewer pre-requisite requirements than those with no previous college education) and 2 + years for the MEPN program.

Cost: $30,000-50,000+ annually depending on program attended.

LVN/LPN Bridge Program

(Licensed Vocational Nurse or Licensed Practical Nurse depending on what state you are in)

This is a route that "bridges" you from being a licensed LVN/LPN to an RN or BSN. LVN/LPN pro-grams are still available but are slowly dying out. They are less difficult to get into, and you attend for approximately 2-3 semesters. LVN/LPN's take a different NCLEX but are still licensed nurses.

To bridge to RN/BSN: Upon completing an LVN program (2-3 semesters), you apply, you join the second year of an RN program at a community college or university. Not all nursing programs offer this, but it's worth checking out.

Example: An LVN with all of the RN pre-reqs completed is accepted to the LVN-RN Bridge program at Pasadena City College and attends the traditional RN class in their second year and graduates with an ADN, and can now take NCLEX for RN.

Difference between LVN and RN: The main difference in what they are allowed to do is with IVs, they are not allowed to administer medication through IVs, and this has resulted in them being phased out of hospital floor nursing roles over the last 20 years. LVN/LPNs are usually utilized in clinic settings. They are paid about 1/2-1/3 what an RN is paid, roughly.

Pros:

- LVN and LVN bridge programs are significantly less impacted; you can work if you have to as an LVN while working on RN/BSN.
- Low-cost route.

- It can be a good option for those who didn't get above a "C" in Science pre-reqs but still passed.

- Having LVN experience may help you get a job as an RN.

Cons:

- Some LVN's who have been working awhile can struggle in bridge programs to becoming an RN.

- This is a long road to becoming an RN and which such a long runway and multiple programs to get through, it would be easier to abandon the end goal.

Timeline: 3-6 semesters for pre-requisites, 2-3 semesters for LVN, 2 semesters to bridge to RN, plus additional 2-3 semesters to get a BSN. Total: 4.5-7 years

Cost: anywhere from free for community college to $50,000+ a year for a private school.

Paramedic/Military option:

There are some programs worth exploring if you have paramedic training and certification. The only one I've ever heard of is in Napa, CA, but they do exist! This is also helpful to know if you were a medic in the military, some of your training credits might count toward your degree.

RN-BSN Bridge programs:

If you get an ADN and become an RN, don't stop! Enroll in a BSN program ASAP. RN-BSN programs are usually around $8-15k but be sure to check if any BSN programs give preferential rates from your particular community college. Also, these programs are sometimes online, and Most RN-BSN programs are designed for working RN's so you can work while in school.

Author Note: With preferred tuition and some help from filling out my FAFSA, my RN-BSN program was $12,000. Totally worth it to research the most cost-effective option for you.

Becoming a Medical Assistant/Surgical Tech first & Transferring:

Becoming a Medical Assistant or Surgical Tech could be a great idea for you to get exposure to the medical community and get your foot in the door of a hospital system. It's important to note that it is not a path to nursing in the sense that you will get credit that will count for nursing classes.

I have seen that there are some private schools that charge a ridiculous amount of money so you can learn to become a Medical Assistant. I think this is wrong of the schools to do this, and I would encourage someone who wants to be an MA to either volunteer at a reputable doctor's office in exchange for job training or go to a community college certificate program.

High School Students:

If you want to get a jump on your nursing school education, take some of the simpler pre-reqs at your local community college over the Summer: Foreign Language, Sociology, Psychology are all great options that won't consume your entire Summer like a Science class might. Read more about specific pre-reqs below and do your own research. They might even count toward your high school credits as well. Check with your high school counselor about this.

After this long list of routes, you probably have one in mind as your best option. No matter which option you choose, all will need to start with the pre-reqs.

Did I miss any routes? Let me know so I can update them.

CHAPTER THREE

NURSING SCHOOL PREREQUISITES

Each school will have a list of requirements that must be completed before you are qualified to apply to their nursing program.

The following classes matter the most. They are the hardest to get into, the hardest to get through. It's important to know that usually, you are only allowed to repeat one of the classes, one time for a better grade. If you fail one of these, your chances of getting into nursing school go down significantly (but it's not impossible):

- Chemistry + Lab (sometimes has an Algebra and English as a pre-req)

- Anatomy + Lab (sometimes has a pre-req)

- Physiology + Lab (Chemistry is usually a pre-req to this)

- Microbiology + Lab (Chemistry is usually a pre-req to this)

Generally speaking, these classes must be in-person, and no online options qualify for nursing science pre-reqs. Unknown if that will change in the future, but it's something to note.

It's vital to know that YOU MUST TAKE THE SCIENCE CLASSES THAT WILL BE ACCEPTED BY NURSING PROGRAMS, it will say it in the class description something like "Meets the requirements for admittance into Nursing program" or the specific class number (e.g., Anatomy 25) will be listed on the nursing school application website as a qualifying class. You cannot just go to any anatomy class; it has to be the right one. The good news is that most approved science classes for one nursing program will be accepted by other nursing programs. But it's your responsibility to check this out. There are a few sites now that help you figure this out (for example, assist.org for California)

Getting into Classes: getting into science pre-req classes can be a challenge no matter what school you go to. Once you have a date/time you can register for classes from your school, you should jump on the computer at midnight or at your assigned registration time if you have one and try to get into whatever science class you can/are qualified to take.

IMPORTANT: You should shoot for A's in these science classes to be competitive for nursing school applications. It can very challenging to do this if you are taking more than one Science class at a time. Especially Physiology and Microbiology in the same semester could be very difficult and could be a risk to your grades. Consider spreading the science classes between three-four semesters so you can to ensure your best grades.

The above paragraph is so vital, I am going to repeat it...

IMPORTANT:You should shoot for A's in these science classes to be competitive for nursing school applications. It can very challenging to do this if you are taking more than one Science at a time. Especially Physiology and Microbiology in the same semester could be very difficult and could be a risk to your grades. Consider spreading the Science classes between three-four semesters if you can to ensure your best grades.

Other Nursing School Pre-Requisites

These are common requirements of many college majors, and so I will not go too in-depth. The grades in these classes matter but not as much as in the sciences. Aim to get a "B" or better in these classes to be a competitive candidate for nursing school, but a "C" in one class will likely not ruin your chances with most nursing schools.

Examples of common General Education College classes that also are required for nursing school.

- English (a certain level of English class, e.g., 1A, sometimes it takes several classes to get to that level)
- Math (usually Algebra II and Statistics depending on the nursing school)
- Speech
- Psychology
- Nutrition
- Foreign Language

The above classes would be a good starting point if you are not committed to the idea of nursing or are not sure about science classes but are working toward some kind of degree. You might as well take the GE (General Education) classes that would count toward nursing school if you go that route or towards an alternative degree.

Each nursing program can have extra or particular class requirements and will list those clearly on their pre-req list. One school I applied to had a special Intro to Nursing class that was required, another wanted Life Span Psychology and another wanted a Religion class. I know in Texas for example you have to take a Texas Government class to get a BSN. These requirements are worth knowing in advance so you aren't surprised.

Hacking your Pre-Reqs:

Some pre-nursing students desire to get as many pre-reqs done in the shortest amount of time. This may not pay off grade-wise, but if you want to do it, you can explore the option of seeing if spots are open for the pre-reqs at other community/junior colleges in your area. An example of this would be taking Anatomy at one school and statistics at another the same semester, or statistics online at a school far away if no in-person attendance is required.

Financial Aid:

Most students know this, but depending on your income and age, you could potentially have all, or a lot of your school paid for you. Depending on the program, you might even get extra cash. It's worth your time to submit a FAFSA app and contact the school's financial aid office about scholarships, grants, and aid.

Success in Sciences Pre-requisites:

The science classes are designed to eliminate the students that will not make it to nursing school. The science pre-reqs, as challenging as they can be, are not as hard as nursing school.

Generally speaking, Anatomy is about practicing and memorizing. You have to put the time in to retain the terms and their locations. Also, in anatomy, you will likely be observing a cadaver and possibly dissecting animal parts.

Chemistry, Physiology, and Microbiology are more about concepts and can be very challenging. It may be worth recording the lectures if you are an auditory learner and listening to them while driving, etc. I often burned the info of these very dry lectures into my brain this way, and I remember reading so many test questions and the answer in my professor's voice played back in my head. Also, a lot of schools, even community colleges, offer free science tutoring, and it is very worth it to attend from the first available session to make sure you do not have gaps in your understanding. To make the most of tutoring, it is best to arrive with questions about topics/chapters you don't understand. Don't expect them to just teach you exactly what you need to know. There are a lot of youtube videos you can search for if you are a visual learner.

What if you get a "C" or flunk a Science Class?

While it would be a lot easier to just get "A's" in the sciences, there are options if you get lower grades. But you will likely pay with a lot of extra time going a roundabout way to being an RN. Probably just better to invest the hard work and long hours in the science classes to get A's.

If you flunk a class or get below a B, each school has its own policy, but as far as I have learned, you are usually allowed to repeat one of the science classes, one time. If you flunk more than one science class, I am pretty sure you are disqualified from nursing programs. This is why you must set yourself up for success and take those classes seriously from the beginning.

Realistic Time Lines:

To get to the point where you can sit for the NCLEX-RN exam, start to finish with no gaps waiting to get into school, will be on average be about 4-5 years whether you do an ADN-RN, BSN, or MEPN program. The timeline will obviously be longer if you don't get into a nursing program the first time you apply.

CHAPTER FOUR

PREPARING TO APPLY

Now that you know your route options, maybe you have gravitated to one route in particular.

Whichever routes you think are best for you, it's worth it to spend an afternoon researching all of the school options in your area or beyond if you are willing to travel/relocate. Find the schools with nursing programs and note down the following:

- School name
- Location
- Length of nursing program
- The degree you will earn
- Application deadline

- Application requirements (letters of rec, experience, volunteer, extra pre-reqs required)
- TEAS/HESI score required
- On a scale of 1-10, how much you like this program

Other Things to Consider when Preparing to Apply

Applying to Out of State Nursing Programs

Applying to out-of-state nursing programs can be a great option for some. If you can be flexible, go for it. It's important to make sure your pre-reqs will be accepted. Most standard science classes with labs will be, but you must verify if you are doing pre-reqs in one state with the goal of a nursing program in another state.

I know an RN who was on track to go right into a nursing program in one state and was accepted. But, she wanted to move back to her home state and start at a nursing program there. She discovered before moving that she would have almost an entire additional semester of state and school-specific pre-reqs, so she opted to stay where she had admission acceptance. Do your research for each school.

Letters of Recommendation

Schools, especially BSN programs and MSN programs, require letters of recommendation written by a professional contact who knows you. These can come from an employer, your supervisor at a volunteer position, a counselor, or a teacher/professor, for example. So start brainstorming who you will need to ask. You may need several letters of recommendation. If you have no one in mind, you will need to create relationships with the people qualified to write a letter of rec by standing out in your science classes, volunteering somewhere, or getting a job. Most nursing programs require the professional to send in the letter themselves sealed or complete it online with a special link sent directly to them. Sufficed to say, it's nearly impossible to get these sent except in a legitimate way.

Personal Statement

This is a good thing to work on while in English class while you are in the writing zone. If a personal statement is required, the school you are applying to will give you a prompt to follow. Personal statements can be good cover letter content so save these for later. Have another person/software proofread it for sentence structure, grammar, and spelling. This is not something that you should do last minute.

Side Job Options

As mentioned before, working as a nurse assistant or tech in the hospital if you have EMT certification is a great option if you need a job while getting through your pre-reqs. Both nurse assistant and tech roles require classes and certification. As mentioned before, this is also a great way to get your foot in the door for your eventual first RN job because often hospitals give hiring priority to current employees.

If you cannot get a job in the medical field, I recommend trying to get a job in customer service. This will be where you have to learn and maintain the skill of making others satisfied with the service you are providing. If you hate doing this, you may not like nursing. Waiting tables, for example, will teach you some serious skills such as: how to build a rapport with someone in minutes, multitask, prioritize, how to time various actions, basically some hard skills that very few inherently possess. Nursing, in some ways, is like being a waiter for meds and medical care. You are the main person the "customer/patient" sees, everything involves you, you coordinate a lot of the patient's care and ensure that it gets done.

Volunteering

Volunteering at a hospital, clinic, or somewhere else is a great option to get your feet wet in the medical field. Many pre-nursing students do this for one of the letters of recommendation that many nursing schools require. Many hospitals and clinics that offer volunteer programs that serve patients have strict attendance rules, specific training, background checks, and interview processes. It takes some work, and many state this clearly when you apply that you will not get a letter of recommendation unless you commit and complete a certain number of hours.

Volunteering is a great way to meet other future nurses and build a support system. I volunteered for years at a Women's Clinic, and I now work with several nurses that I volunteered with. Your volunteer buddies are your future colleagues and it's a great start in networking. You never know who could help you land a job in the future.

TEAS TEST/ HESI/other Admittance Tests

Most four-year schools require either the TEAS test or HESI. These are third-party tests that nursing schools use as part of the selection process. There are books you can get to prep you for it. You take the test at specific sites. Nursing school websites will tell you what their cut-off is on test scores to qualify to apply. While these tests aren't super hard, in my opinion, they are super long. Practice testing and going at an optimal time for you to perform well on the test is advised. Some schools allow you to repeat the test, and then they combine your two scores. Also, sometimes it takes a while to get a test date, so register and then study! If you are not strong in a particular subject, like math, plan on taking the test after you wrap up your math pre-reqs. The test results are usually good for a few years but check the tests official website regarding the rules.

Last Tips for Applying to Programs

Once you have your list of schools and the dead-lines, you will be organized to know which schools need your application by when.

When the application period opens, get on it and submit well before the deadline, this allows for questions, website problems to be resolved, etc.

Fill out the general application, resume, personal statement, etc. Submit transcripts and test results.

Get your letters of recommendation sent in by those who have agreed to write them for you. Follow up nicely with the people writing them that they were sent in. It's not enough to just ask and get their agreement to do it, confirm! These professional contacts are busy and sometimes need to be reminded. If you do not follow up, you could risk having an incomplete application, and the nursing program you applied to won't consider you.

Conclusion to Part I

When your applications are complete, you can cross your fingers and settle in to wait. In the meantime, work, save up money if you can, and get any other general education classes you need for your degree out of the way.

PART II

SUCCEEDING IN NURSING SCHOOL

You got into nursing school! Congrats! Now you need to prepare your life, so you will succeed.

Note: If you don't get in your first round of applications, know that you are not alone, this is quite common. I would recommend giving it another try and broadening the scope of where you apply. Schools often are aware when you apply a second time. I have yet to meet a nurse who didn't get into any school by Round 2 of applications if they were qualified. Try not to get too disheartened; this lag in time will be a bump in the rearview mirror soon enough.

CHAPTER FIVE

NURSING SCHOOL-LECTURE AND EXAMS

Here's the thing about nursing school. You are expected to learn a massive amount of content in a relatively short period of time. In my opinion, it's impossible to retain it all, but fortunately, it's broken into subjects in most schools.

Most if not all nursing programs have several components or types of learning that happen each week: Lecture, Lab & Clinical. And we'll break each part down with some tips and tricks.

Lectures and exams:

If you have gotten this far in your education, you very likely have sorted out how to study and pass tests. But be aware nursing school requires a different level and type of retention and test-taking. It's impossible to just memorize; you have to learn concepts and have a conceptual understanding of the material. Even more importantly, you have to be good at understanding the test questions being asked. For each test question, there are likely two correct answers to your four or more options, and even though two are correct, one is the better answer. Therefore, you will only get credit for one of the answers. Annoying right?

It's advised to not get overconfident about the material. Even if you think the content is easy, you must study because the test questions are specifically written to throw you off and confuse you. If the question seems really simple and straightforward, you might be missing something. Or maybe it is just an easy question. It's tricky.

If you don't learn the content assigned, you won't be able to think on your feet during a test. The test questions are written to decipher if you learned the content. I have seen plenty of people flunk out because they were overconfident and didn't study enough. I never walked into a test confidently, I only walked in knowing that I gave it my best effort to learn the assigned chapters.

At least when I was in school, failing a test in a nursing class usually meant you got lower than a 75%, which in most other classes would be a passing C grade...not in nursing school. Usually, a test also has a point value, and the points add up cumulatively over the semester or class subject.

Example:

Test 1 =55 points

Test 2=75 points

Midterm =150 points

Test 4=70 points

Final =150 points

Total: 500 points

In this example let's say a passing grade for the class is getting 375 points out of the total 500.

So if you only have 125 points to miss the entire semester and you bomb or miss a test, you have less grace in what you can miss on all future tests. This point system isn't unique, a lot of college classes and subjects use this grading system, but when the cut-off is 75%, the stakes are raised.

Early in my RN program, I overheard a classmate stating that the content of our psych class was a joke. He thought it was so easy! The next week, he flunked his test and flunked it so badly he was right on the edge of failing until the end of that unit. He couldn't catch up and didn't pass. This is a level of stress that is hard to describe when you have worked so hard to get where you are, and you are on edge for weeks just to fail.

Give the first few weeks of studying a subject everything you've got. If you do really well, then you'll know that's what it takes. If you don't do well, you will need to step up your game. But out of the gate, go hard, so you do not start with a low grade that you are constantly trying to make up for.

Usually, you go through an entire subject/area of nursing and have corresponding clinicals. For example, in one semester, you may take Intermediate Med-Surg, Labor and Delivery, and Pediatrics. You take these subjects consecutively. Meaning, you take Int. Med Surg, while concurrently going to clinicals on a Med Surg floor for a certain number of weeks. Then you take the final for Int. Med Surg and pass or fail. If you pass, you move on to studying L&D and going to L&D clinicals. The advantage is that you are focusing on certain body systems and particular types of nursing and not all over the place. But, if you flunk one of these classes, the majority of schools will not let you continue or finish the semester.

More on Nursing School Tests:

Nursing exam questions are weird. They're timed, and they're proctored, and at some schools, they are on school-provided computers. You're watched like a hawk, sometimes you're allowed one piece of scratch paper that they provide for you, so you can't bring in your own cheat material apparently. Some have rules like, if they see your phone during a test, you automatically fail. Each school has its own set of rules. Just follow them. Don't crack jokes before or during a test; just follow the rules.

The most important thing to focus on a test question is how to decipher exactly what the question is asking you. This sounds obvious, but it's harder than you think. The test question might be 3-4 sentences long but what you need to answer pertains especially to three words at the end of the question. The questions are designed like this because it is how the nursing board exam (aka NCLEX) questions are written.

Once you have an idea of what they are asking, read all of the answers. Even if option B sounds right, option D could be an even better option. After reading all of the answers, some students have the most success with eliminating the answers they know are wrong and then going with what seemed like the best answer. This isn't revolutionary advice, but it's important you understand that the test questions are designed to trick you, and you should be ready for that.

Lastly, keep in mind that the majority of students enrolled in nursing school pass, and you likely will too if you do the work.

Warming Up for Tests

It's important to get yourself in the correct mindset to do well on nursing school tests. Take some time to sort out what that is for you. Whatever will help your brain function best, is best. These tests are like a mental version of a game or track meet. So let's figure out how you should prepare before a test.

For me, it went like this: I would have studied all I can in the days prior to the test but I'd cut it off at around 7pm the night before the exam. I would watch a no-drama TV show. Nothing that would keep me awake. I would go to sleep as early as possible and wake up extra early, so I wasn't rushed. The night before, I would lay out everything I would need, bag packed, water bottle filled, clothes laid out, shower night before so I wouldn't have to think at all on the morning of the test. This was to preserve valuable brain space and power. I would eat a really big breakfast so I wouldn't have a chance of getting hungry mid a 2-hour mentally exhausting exam. My friend in school couldn't eat anything, so it's whatever works for you. Normally I would drink coffee at home, but before a test, I got a 3 shot espresso drink which gave me a buzz that worked in my favor. Then I would listen to music in the car on my drive that was motivating. The point is, I found a ritual that my brain recognized as a time to perform my best. I am not suggesting you follow my routine, I am suggesting you make your own.

If this seems excessive, it's because one failed test (i.e., below 75%) can really mess you up putting your entire future on the line, so it's worth it to give extra consideration to this.

Another question to ask yourself is what time of day do you perform best? Study then.

What type of foods/drinks help you think clearest/sharpest? Eat these foods before a test, drink that before a test. I'm suggesting you do not drink alcohol the night before a test, if you must drink, drink after a test. It is not worth it if it will even slightly cloud your judgment.

Amphetamines: Ritalin, Adderall, etc. are utilized by many students to do well on tests with or without a prescription. I am not recommending these but if you do take them, know that nursing schools are known to randomly drug screen students. Amphetamines show up on a drug screen, and you can be expelled. I highly recommend seeking treatment and help if you depend on these for success in school or, at minimum, having a note from your doctor if prescribed.

Pre-Test Checklist

Again, this helps preserve valuable brain power and decision-making for tests.

What tasks could you get done the night before the test?

- Shower
- Clothes laid out for that day

- Gas in car/ride arranged/plan to leave extra early for pubic transport delays
- Backpack packed so you can grab and go,
- Test notes and class materials pre-packed
- Food and coffee plan

Getting things ready the night before helps with tests, clinicals, job interviews, and your first RN job. Take any possible task from the big day off of your plate by prepping the night before to allow the most brain power for the day when you need it the most.

Sleep: Most nursing students are tired all the time. There is never enough time to study, clinical days are long, etc. You still need to build sleep into your schedule. It should be a priority over social plans, content consumption, etc. Work out a plan to get as much sleep as possible!

Tips for Success in Nursing School:

Through trial and error going through it myself and seeing my classmates, these are the points that I think make the biggest impact on nursing school success:

- Always show up on time
- Be willing to cooperate with the expectations of your instructors and have a good, positive attitude

- Figure out the rules for classes, tests, and clinicals (do this by always paying attention and take notes when an instructor is speaking to you and your class, read all handouts and emails from school, ask your classmates, ask your instructors if you can't figure it out from the above suggestions)

- Do exactly what is asked of you in class and in clinicals

- Pass your tests, get through clinicals

Also, try to be professional. What does this mean in class? This means having outward facing manners, appearing respectful. Don't talk to your friends during a lecture, don't scroll your phone, try to say good morning, smile, being interested in the content, do your work, ask questions that pertain to the material, help others, ask for help in a nice way. Even if you don't feel like it, this is exactly what you have to do as an RN all the time, being outwardly polite and professional even if you don't want to.

Know that there is very little hand-holding in nursing school classes. Sink or swim is a common attitude from professors and administrators. You will have to figure stuff out on your own at times or with your fellow students. Be friendly and make friends. Ask questions until you understand the rules and follow them strictly. Know that the strict rules are to weed out the people who cannot follow instructions. I think that the theory behind this is that if you cannot follow a teacher's instructions, you probably will not follow a doctor's, putting a patient's life at risk.

Expect that there will be some disorganization in your program and amongst some teachers. You have to advocate for yourself if something isn't right for you, for example, if they forget to assign you to a clinical group. Don't assume the administrative staff or teachers will figure out your problems, even if it's their error. Be proactive but polite. Try to be flexible; expect it to be unorganized. If it's not affecting your grade or your grad date, consider letting it go and trying to roll with it.

Lastly, there is really no point in spending your time complaining, every nursing school seems to have flaws. Don't be too negative about whatever annoyance happens that week; otherwise, your class can become toxic, and the teachers will turn against your class. Your instructors will get to know you better than in most other instructor student relationships, and seriously, if they like you, they will help you a lot more if you get on shaky ground. But if they don't like you, they will have no problem flunking anyone that is on the line between passing and failing. This happened to several students in my nursing class.

Make Friends

On my first day of anatomy class, lab class, specifically, I was challenging myself to be more friendly. I promised myself that I would say "hi" and chat with whoever sat down at my table. Sufficed to say, 10+ years later, that person that I said "hi" to is one of my closest friends. We talk many times a week and are both L&D nurses. We have talked each other off of the ledge of quitting many times. So minimally during those first few days of class, I would highly recommend putting your phone away, looking friendly, and saying "hi."

Working while in a Nursing Program:

Most schools discourage applicants from working while in nursing school. Even if you are the smartest, most time efficient person, it will be very, very challenging for you to do both. Ideally, you can figure out how to just attend school for the four-five semesters when you are in the actual nursing school part of your education. For pre-reqs, it's realistic to work part-time or even full time, but while in nursing school you will be putting your ability to pass on the line.

This may seem impossible, you might feel that you just have to earn money. As a former student with little income, I totally get it. But if you do work concurrently with school, you will run the risk of flunking a class. The penalty for this is usually sitting out the following semester. And then, only if there is space the semester after that will you be allowed back. And, you will repeat the semester you failed. Meaning, you will be a year behind in the best scenario. Only you can decide what is best for you but know the potential consequences of working while in school.

Exception for working RNs with ADN degrees: For those doing the community college route who get ADN. After you are an RN, there are BSN Bridge programs that are designed for working nurses. So know that it's totally doable if you want to work while continuing on to get a BSN.

Every single person I ever knew who flunked a class in nursing school had a side job. It's a risk if you try to do both. I worked part-time initially in nursing school. I passed my Pediatrics final and class by one test question. One question! Seriously, if I had answered it differently, who knows where I would be now. I learned my lesson and sorted out to get financial help for the rest of my program so I could do better. And I did.

How to Deal if you do Fail a Nursing Class:

If you do fail a class, whether you are working or not, here are some emergency management tips:

0. I know this really sucks, but it doesn't have to be the end of your nursing journey. Another classmate of mine failed the third semester by a single percentage point and was allowed back immediately the next semester because of her positive track record in school, and she is a kick-ass nurse now.

1. Whether it is your fault or you think it's because an instructor didn't like you (has happened before), do NOT say or put anything in writing to your school or professors that will burn bridges or get you expelled from the program. You must try to be as professional as possible. The further you are in the program, the more likely you could potentially squeeze into the next semester, so again, don't ruin your chances with the instructor or Dean who may try to do you a favor by pointing your finger at someone else.

2. If you are calm enough after learning that you flunked, go speak to the professor ask for guidance as to what the next steps are. You might have been told by the professor privately and allowed to look at your exam. I suggest doing this so you won't wonder later on if something was missed. Ask to speak to the Dean and get his/her guidance. If you are not calm, consider leaving campus to get some space and cool off. Email your professors ASAP, so they know you are remorseful and take responsibility for what happened and that you do not want to give up on your dream.

3. For uncontrollable tears, drink water, take Vitamin B1 if you cannot stop crying (weird, but it works for some), and going for a walk might help.

Ok, so you have some understanding of what to expect from nursing classes and exams. Next, we'll talk about an even more painful part of nursing school, at least for me.

Further Help: Find a list of recommended books and resources for studying nurse school content at nursehelpdesk.com

CHAPTER SIX

NURSING SCHOOL-CLINICALS

Clinicals are small groups of nursing students with one clinical instructor that is a registered nurse. Possibly it's one of your lecture professors. Your group descends on a floor of a hospital and each student follows around an assigned, hopefully kind, floor nurse. You help provide care to the patients; it is supposed to be hands-on learning.

Clinicals are a mixture of menial work, seeing some cool stuff, hopefully learning some things, being sorta bored at times and looking awkward. Know that school and clinical instructors think of it like it's your job, and as such, they expect you to behave a certain way. Many clinical instructors do not care if they flunk you, they see it as their obligation to make sure someone lazy doesn't join their ranks. Schools are not legally allowed to let you graduate if you have not completed the required clinical hours, so they are mandatory. Usually, there is wiggle room for you to miss one or two clinical days a semester, but I would save those for emergencies, and you must check your own school rules. These are not going to be the best or the most fun days of your life. But here are some things I wish I had known and things that I really want to say to all of the students who I've seen on the floors where I work.

Learning Curve:

It's likely that you will not be good at many nursing skills out of the gate. This is why you have clinicals and labs. It's ideal to practice as many skills as you can in this setting, so try to be confident and hustle up opportunities where you can practice. Don't worry about looking incompetent in school or at clinical with skills; this is where you learn.

Special ways to piss off your clinical instructor:

Being late even by a minute. Even if you have a fantastic reason. Just know that you have to follow the rules very strictly, or you won't make it. Even if the rules seem lame. Nothing will substitute for showing up, doing the work, and following the rules.

Disappearing from your assigned unit. Unless you are an approved break, if you go MIA, your whole day could be wiped and won't count toward your required hours. There was a student on my floor who went to take a nap in her car during lunch and essentially overslept for several hours. I believe she was eventually expelled. All of those years of work down the drain because of a nap!

Falling asleep at the nurses' station. This also happened to a classmate of mine, and she was kicked out of the program in the final weeks of school.

I recently walked past a nursing student in the hallway just outside a patient room, sitting on the windowsill, on Facetime, sipping a drink under her mask. She was talking loudly and possibly arguing with her significant other or friend. Presumably, she was on her break, but this was concerning for several reasons. One, personal phone calls shouldn't happen on a patient floor; if they must happen while you are on clinicals, even on your break, it needs to be in the breakroom, outside, or worst case, the bathroom. This is such basic common sense that it seriously makes me question this student's judgment, and I would absolutely not allow this student to even take water to my patient unattended.

Working with a Floor RN

For clinicals, you will be assigned to work with an RN that is employed and working on the floor. You will follow them around and hopefully learn from them. Nurses work really hard most of the time, they have practiced for years on how to be the most efficient with their time, and this practice allows them to get all of their work done. Having a nursing student follow them around is a bit like having an additional patient; it's a lot of extra work for them. They don't know you, they don't trust you, and you mess with their flow. Also, explaining and teaching you all day is exhausting, and they don't get any extra pay. Anything that happens to you or their patient because of you is on them and this heightens the stress of the day.

But...if you are useful, help the RN and floor get through the day, then you will learn. It's implied that you will be beside your assigned nurse, so be prepared to just follow them around. Don't wait to be beckoned every time the nurse goes into a patient room. They will tell you when not to follow them, like to the bathroom.

0. Be ready with pens, small safe scissors, stethoscope and paper. Ideally arrive before report. (Report is the passing of info of patient's conditions, history and plan of care, from one nurse to the next. Usually done at change of shift) You should have some goals in mind for the day e.g. "IVs, seeing the stages of labor, newborn assessments, tele monitoring,

helping with CPR compressions," come up with something that pertains to the unit you are on that day. The nurse will probably ask you what you can do, what you want to do; they are feeling you out, so saying something like, "Skill-wise, I really want to work on drawing blood if anyone is willing to show me, I also haven't gotten the hang of back priming piggybacks so it would be cool to see that, as far as in the ER today, I am hoping to learn about some acute conditions and how to spot the signs and symptoms of those. I am also very good at fetching supplies and ice."

Keep it short, don't chat too much unless prompted. You are there to observe and be helpful. Chit-chat has a time and place on the floor, and you haven't learned when that is yet.

1. Have a good attitude and introduce yourself. "Hi, I'm 'name' I'll be your nursing student today." Listen to the report and write down as much as you can. Do NOT say that you can remember everything about the patient without writing it down. This just shows us that you don't care.

2. After the report, if you can squeeze it in, show gratitude for their time, "I really appreciate you taking me as a student today, I know it adds to your work load, I'll do everything I can to be useful, I want to work." Even if they are not effusive, they will likely appreciate

the initial acknowledgment, gratitude and willingness to help.

3. Nurses have a very keen lazy radar. As soon as we spot a lazy student, we will probably ignore you.

We had students on our floor one day, and my assigned student was in the OR observing a C-Section. Another student was sitting at the nurse's station on his phone. I was really busy, and asked, "Can you do something for me?" and he looked up, paused and said, "that depends."

Me in my head: "Forget you." I had no time for this, my patient was about to deliver her baby, and I needed something from the linen closet, and once he got it for me, I was going to bring him in for my delivery. I got mad and said, "Forget it."

He ran after me after 15 seconds, realizing he messed up and was like, "What do you need?"I was done, "it's ok," and I ran into my delivery, leaving him to continue scrolling on his phone.

Gosh, people! Contribute! Help the floor! Have a good attitude! As a student, you might be asked to fetch stuff, don't be offended. RNs ask each other to grab stuff all day long when we are tied up with a patient. We as nurses are constantly getting supplies, sheets, ice for each other's patients. Seriously, get used to it.

Help the CNA! Help the Nurses! Just do it. Your day will go a lot faster. Also, the CNA's remember

the standouts and totally have the power to recommend you to a nurse manager. And, they could
be your co-workers one day. Even doctors and
managers help the nurses with little tasks when
they are slammed. Do not for one second think
that you as a nursing student are above doing
grunt work. If you do, you are not in the right field.

Nurse Realness

This is my own personally developed work
philosophy after many years, but I truly
believe it is the expectation of most nursing
units. This applies to school, clinicals, and
really any job to take in the future:

Giving your best effort truly pays off.
Whether you care, whether you contribute,
whether you are lazy or give more than
expected, these things are noted by your
peers, co-workers, and those above you
(instructors, managers, doctors). Usually, your
behavior is observed silently. Very rarely will
you get bad feedback from others to your face.
Sometimes you will get good feedback but do
not expect more than a "thanks for your help."
In the real world, people are forming
opinions about you, and usually, these are
not shared with you; they are shared with
others. Your feedback comes from others'
willingness to help you. Teamwork is essential
and if you go the extra mile for someone else, it
will come back to you. Your success in
clinicals and in your job as an RN is largely

based on others' opinions of your work and how you conduct yourself.

Please remove complaining from your vocabulary when you are a student nurse on the floor because no one cares. Everyone is tired. If you have true safety concerns or issues, please communicate with them. Whining? Keep it to yourself.

Many of us (floor nurses) like helping student nurses, but we also get annoyed at those who are lazy, not interested in helping, and not professional.

When you become a nurse giving full effort is most noticed by the people that matter, the patients. I cannot tell you how far it goes when your patient sees that you are working hard for them. You will learn how exactly to do this as you get through your new grad years, but it's a good idea to start practicing putting in the full effort now.

Things that contribute to the floor RN's not liking you (if you care):

- Complaining about how tired you are
- Taking our chairs when we need to chart
- Disappearing when we have a skill to teach you
- Scrolling your phone a lot
- Acting like you know everything
- Not expressing gratitude for the nurse's time

Sadly, the above traits are common. You, as someone who cares, can use this to your advantage. You will shine when you are a super helpful and positive nursing student. **Note:** This shouldn't happen but if a preceptor completely ignores you, is rude or ditches you, hopefully you can find ways to be useful to the floor, ask the CNAs how you can help them to make the day go by. Talk to your preceptor if you feel safe doing so and keep in mind that this is not on you and there is nothing wrong with you, it's about them.

5 Ways to Get Kicked out of Nursing School BESIDES FLUNKING YOUR TESTS:

1. Post anything, anything about a patient on the internet. Photos obviously, but also any description, anything. Beyond a pic of you in the BR in scrubs, don't do it. (Unless it's work specific issue with my manager for a very good reason and on a secure communication line, I never ever write out things electronically about a patient outside of charting)

2. Talk about a patient in the halls

3. Be late or don't show up to Clinicals

4. Be late or don't show up to SIM (explained soon)

5. Do anything wrong with a med administration. You should be sweating bullets the first

time you give meds and following all instructions to the letter.

Clinical Care Plans

I almost forgot about these. I must have blocked them out of my memory. These are tedious writing and research exercises that you do to learn meds, medical conditions, how to care for these conditions, and how it all ties together. They get easier as the semesters pass but overall are a lot of work. Ensure you block out enough time for these. If you wait until the last minute, you could be working all night to get these done. They are very time-consuming. In real life these *are* part of charting but take about 5 seconds to do.

Preceptorship

Usually, during a BSN or MSN program, you will do a preceptorship on a floor with a nurse that has agreed to exclusively train you on the floor with them for several weeks. You will follow their schedule, and you have a checklist from your school of what you need to get done. You will likely do this in your last semester. Usually, preceptees have the how-to be professional part down and understand that the stakes are higher and that they may have a chance of getting a New Grad spot on that floor.

Other Hot Clinical Tips:

C-diff or just poop smell that lingers in your nose can be "wiped" out with an alcohol swab. Literally, wipe out your nose with an alcohol wipe. It burns but passes quickly. I started doing this during Covid, too, because it made me feel better psychologically.

Forgot deodorant? Hand sanitizer applied to the area gets rid of the smell. Please wash your hands after. Please.

Standing for as long as nurses do takes some getting used to. The right shoes and socks go a long way in keeping you comfortable. Sneakers usually work best with insoles, compression socks help, medical clogs, for some. I like Calzuros. My best trick at the end of the day is to lay on my bed or the ground and put my legs straight up a wall. This helps return all the blood that pooled in your legs and feet. I always feel better the next morning when I do this vs. when I forget. It also prevents varicose veins and relieves tired feet. Magnesium foot soak is also helpful for feet that hurt.

Feel faint? Dizzy, disoriented, hot, nauseous are all signs that you are going to be passing out shortly. Smell an alcohol wipe, lean against a wall and slide down, sit on your butt until someone finds you. The most important thing is to sit down somewhere, so you don't hit your head. Tell someone if you can. You won't get in trouble for fainting. It is quite common.

No Call, No Show

Pretty much in any job, and definitely in nursing, a "No Call, No Show" is bad. This means you didn't show up for your shift and you didn't call to let them know. The only valid excuse for this would be where you or your loved one is in a verifiable emergency. I had a co-worker who was T-boned in her car on the way to her shift and was taken via ambulance to the trauma ER of the hospital where she worked. Anything other than that level of emergency, you could get put on probation, fired, or at the least, an written warning for not calling out sick. Know that if you "No Call, No Show" to clinicals, you will possibly get expelled from the program. Expelled meaning, you won't ever be allowed back into the program.

SIM Lab

Hopefully, this book has impressed upon you how seriously you should take clinicals. You should probably take SIM lab even more seriously. SIM or Simulation Lab is basically a varying degree of mock patient setups, usually in a Code or Rapid Response situation. For some reason, the teachers and clinical instructors seem to treat SIM lab like life or death. This is another instance where there should be a huge priority given to showing up early, paying attention to the rules, following those rules, and cooperating. A classmate of mine showed up 2 hours late for our clinical group's SIM lab session. She didn't call the instructor, she only texted a classmate she was running late. Then when she arrived with wet hair, she told the instructor she wasn't feeling well. It was considered a no-call, no-show, and she failed that class. I don't know if she was allowed back either, and my clinical instructor had zero sympathy for her.

Bottom Line and Wrap-Up

Ultimately we want you to show respect for where you are and what we are doing. Keep in mind that you are being a witness to people at their most vulnerable and that must be respected. If you show up, cooperate, be professional and safe with patients, do what is asked of you, contribute and help, you will pass clinicals. Concurrently, study well, pass your tests, do your work, and you'll make it through school.

Further Reading: *Nursing School Thrive Guide* by Maureen Osuna

CHAPTER SEVEN

PREPARING FOR NCLEX

You made it! Or maybe you are very close to making it to the end of nursing school. Endless congratulations on completing something that many can't. The next step is NCLEX. You learned all of the content you need for the board exam, now comes passing it.

Understand the Beast

It often takes a few months to get from graduation day to NCLEX testing day. This is because the paperwork and requirements that your particular state requires for you to sit for NCLEX come from you and your school separately and takes awhile to be processed. Every state is different in its timelines, and your school should have some insight into this. Some schools really drag their feet to get all of the requirements to the board of nursing. Usually, in the last semester of nursing school, your teachers will help you understand what you personally need to submit and by what date. Don't sleep on this, get it done before the deadline.

Criminal Records

We know that people with felonies most of the time are not allowed to become nurses. Charges less than a felony must be disclosed to the Board of Registered Nursing (BRN) when you are applying to take NCLEX. I knew one classmate who had a misdemeanor from years prior. She followed the rules of disclosure as outlined by the BRN and explained with facts exactly what happened. As far as the outcome, I know that she is a nurse at one of the best hospitals in California, so obviously, the BRN let her test. I have heard of stories where student nurses did not disclose their minor criminal records, the BRN did a search on them, and they were barred from becoming a nurse because they did not disclose their records.

Studying for NCLEX

There are a lot of study guides and options out there. I personally think the best use of your time and money is getting access to a practice test question bank and taking practice tests on your computer over and over for long sets of time, like a mock NCLEX test. I used Uworld, but I am sure there are more options out there now.

The same rules for test-taking apply when taking NCLEX, get everything ready the night before. Sleep well, eat well and pick a test time that is during your prime performance period. Give yourself plenty of time to get there. Take anything off of your plate from test day and do it the night before.

While waiting for your Test Date

Get yourself ready physically for the job. Anyone in good shape should be fine. If you are more sedentary right now, you might want to consider a walking regimen to work up to 15k steps a day at least three times a week. Squats are also a good idea as you will be crouching on the floor at times, and you super do not want your knees to touch the floor. Gross. It's very possible that once you walk on the floor for a shift, you could be standing for 12 hours straight.

Should you apply for jobs before or after NCLEX?

Many applications for New Graduate Hospital Training programs say that you must have NCLEX passed before starting your job, but not before applying. Some hospitals anticipate that New Grads will apply before getting their license with the rule that if you don't pass NCLEX after they a hire you, you won't be able to start working.

It's important to start applying in the last semester of your nursing program for a New Grad Program that will start when you feasibly will have passed NCLEX. For example, if you graduate in May 2025, you would apply before graduation, say in February 2025, for a New Grad Program starting in September 2025. Make sense? Most New Grad Programs start in the Spring and Fall to give recent graduates that time to pass NCLEX. **Note:** Some hospital applications are only open for one day to mitigate the number of applications they get. Having your resume and cover letter ready to go to customize for each job app makes applying easier. We'll discuss resume and cover letter in Part III.

Game Plan

Set aside 10-20 minutes each day to stalk the hiring websites of the hospitals in your area to be able to apply immediately when an application period opens. There are many FB groups too that post job opportunities. Search for one in your area.

Ok, so get your test date, practice taking the test, take the test, pass NCLEX (yay!), all while looking for and maybe starting to apply for jobs...now what?

PART III

YOUR FIRST RN JOB

Congrats RN! Now we need to get you a job. Part III covers a lot of ground and will help get you on your way to success as a working nurse

CHAPTER EIGHT

LANDING AND PREPARING FOR YOUR FIRST JOB

The most common and probably most coveted first RN job out of school in the U.S. is a spot in a New Grad Program. We will be discussing these programs in much more detail in addition to other first year job options. From there, you'll learn where and how to start your search.

Overview of New Grad Programs

When hired into a new grad program, it is understood that you have never worked as an RN in a hospital. Hospitals usually only hire New Grad RNs that have graduated within the last year and have not worked as an RN for more than a few months (typically six or less). For example, after passing NCLEX, you start at a Laser hair removal job or in a psych facility for a few months, you would still qualify for a new grad job in a hospital. However, if you worked in a Skilled Nursing Facility for three years as an RN, you likely will not be qualified to be part of a New Grad Program.

New Grad Programs are ideal because they set you up as best as possible to succeed in the hospital. Hospitals invest a lot of time in you, so you are safe enough to care for patients. Often you are on orientation for 6 weeks-6 months. You will likely get paid less than when you are on your own.

Some New Grad Programs ask that you agree either verbally or in writing to stick around for a least a year or two. I do not think they can legally require you to stay but double-check your own agreements. I have heard of some "contracts" where you agree to pay the money back that they invested in you if you leave sooner than agreed.

Many nurses I worked with from my new grad program cohort left my floor/unit after a year. I also transferred to another department after a year. It's common, but I feel bad for the floors that have a constant revolving door of taking newbie nurses and raising them to be functioning on their own, all to have them leave for better pay, more specialized floor, and better work conditions. I see both sides. It's generally considered poor form to leave before a year, but it's your decision. If it's a toxic work environment or your mental health is suffering, you have to weigh the pros vs. cons and ultimately do what's best for you.

Note for RNs with Associates Degrees: Let's say you get your ADN-RN and are unable to get a hospital new grad job. You end up working in an SNF or other outside-the-hospital RN position, and you go past the year mark of being out of school. If you then go get your BSN, you'll be considered a New Grad again!

Hospital RN Jobs without a New Grad Program

Some hospitals do not offer structured New Grad Programs but have long orientation periods. These can be a good option as well. I would be wary of an orientation period of just 2-3 weeks, but positions that offer 6-8+ weeks of training will help you get your footing. An online search or post to a new grad forum may give good insight if a particular program sets you up for success or failure.

Feeling Prepared

I don't know if I have met anyone who came out of their orientation period that was confident in their abilities to be a competent nurse. The truth is that you have to do your best to improve and give your all each day. That's all you can do. Dread, fear, even feeling ill is unfortunately normal for new grads and even seasoned nurses. Managing stress is something you'll be working on how to handle your entire career. It gets so much easier as time goes on, and you will learn what to expect from scary situations.

Other Types of RN jobs

Below are some ideas for nurses who don't want to work in the hospital. Hospitals certainly aren't for everyone. It's important to note if you decide you later do want to work in a hospital down the road, it can be very challenging to get accepted into a New Grad Program (as these are designed for new grads and offer the most training). It is far more common for experienced floor nurses to transition to outpatient/clinic than the other way, but it's not impossible.

I am not an expert in these areas as I haven't experienced them personally, but here's what I do know.

Aesthetics RN: From laser hair removal to botox, there are definite roles for RN in the aesthetic space. Advice from above still applies while you are in school. I had some schoolmates who worked for a med spa office as a medical assistant or receptionist while taking pre-reqs, built connections, etc., and went straight to a docs office after passing NCLEX. I know nurses who do laser on the side of their hospital jobs for extra money.

In many cities, there is also training that you can do to learn how to inject botox, fillers, etc.

Telehealth, triage, insurance, etc.: Often having the nursing judgment required for these jobs comes from experience working in a hospital. However, some companies hire New Grads, especially insurance companies. It's my understanding that you work in an office space or from home. You are on the phone a lot and filling out lots of information online, i.e., data entry and helping folks with claim determination or questions about their health.

Clinic RN: An RN will be hired in a clinic setting when that clinic needs someone who can perform RN-specific skills. Often they are looking for someone who can start IVs with their eyes closed, knows how to give chemo, juggle nursing tasks, and doesn't need a ton of hand-holding on how to be a nurse. Sometimes, Clinic RN's are the leaders or supervisors of other less trained health care personnel. I am not saying you can't land a Clinic RN job out of school, and I have seen one or two job listings over the years for New Graduate Clinic positions, but they are often the harder opportunities to come by. Also, a lot of experienced RN's go for clinic jobs when they are burned out on floor nursing, so you could be competing with seasoned nurses in the application process.

School Nursing: Some states require a special school nurse certificate. I know a few nurses who were offered jobs in schools while doing their community health rotation during their BSN programs.

Travel Nursing: If you haven't heard of travel nursing, the idea is that you sign and arrange with a third party agency to work in a hospital for approximately 13 weeks. You typically make more money than you would being a career or permanent employee at a hospital. There are many resources online that go over the pros and cons of such a role. If you can do it, it can be a great way to explore new areas. You must have a certain amount of verifiable experience before they will hire you.

Outpatient surgery: This could be in a freestanding surgical center or one affiliated with a hospital. You will function as either a pre-op, post op or intra operative (or all three!) nurse and they should train you. Patients usually go home with a few hours after surgery. I did this as a side job before getting into L&D and I liked it a lot.

More RN jobs options for New Graduates:

Skilled Nursing Facilities, Dialysis, Substance Abuse Treatment/ Eating Disorder Treatments/ Rehabs, Psychiatric Facilities, Jails/ Prisons, Did I miss any? Do you have experience with these types of jobs? Please send me your advice and experience at nursehelpdesk.com.

CHAPTER NINE

FINDING A JOB

The fear of not being able to secure an RN job is instilled in student nurses from nearly day one of nursing school. This is a valid concern as there are many qualified applicants that try for each New Grad position.

If you go into the process knowing that it's likely to take awhile, even with hard work, to get a job, you'll beat yourself up a lot less. It requires a combination of hustling and patience.

You can attempt to increase your luck by figuring out how to get a manager's eye on your application in various ways. Some ways might be having a personal contact that can help get your name/resume to a hiring manager, being an existing employee with a hospital or clinic, having a

BSN vs. ADN, having certain certifications beyond your RN license (BLS, ACLS, PALS, NRP, etc.), can all possibly help you stand out. But don't get too discouraged if you don't have any of that.

There is no magical or guaranteed way to get a New Grad position or RN job. Nearly every employed nurse from the last 5-10 years I've asked said that they applied for many many many jobs and had an average of 6 months between graduation and starting in an RN role. Try not to get discouraged. Put in a lot of effort, and you'll most likely get there. Every one of the nurses I know or kept up with from school got jobs. Mostly because they persisted until it happened.

It's smart to apply for every program you can and are qualified for. How far are you willing to drive? Are you willing to relocate? Cast as wide of a net as you can and are willing to go. Most likely, if you can only get a job out of town or out of state, you will only need a year of experience before being qualified for an experienced nurse position closer to home.

Which floor/job will give you the most options?

Rarely does a new grad nurse get immediately into their dream specialty at their dream hospital, but it does happen occasionally. If you cannot go directly into your dream specialty, a year on a telemetry or med-surg floor will more than likely turn you into a fully functioning nurse, and from there, you can build on your experience to learn another specialty of nursing. It can be a painful process but very valuable for your overall career.

Your first year as a New Grad on a hospital floor will:

1. Make you are far better nurse

2. Help you learn how to effectively communicate with doctors, management, and other members of the team, which is often critical for the best outcomes for your patients

3. Know how to spot that a patient is in trouble

4. Teach you time management

5. How to group tasks, batch work and cluster care

If you are not sure what area of the hospital you like? You can always start in tele/med-surg and switch if it's too much or you hate it. Worst case, you get some valuable skills that will help you your entire career and can launch you into the ER, ICU, L&D, Cath Lab. Peds, NICU, etc.

Author Note

I started in telemetry. And while it turned out to be not for me, I learned all of the above and more. Before I started in tele, I was sure I wanted to go to the ED or ICU, I was wrong, but I had to work as an RN, caring for sick adults to know. I worked with some really amazing nurses, and after a year, I was able to convince L&D to train me on the recommendation of the tele educator. I have been able to help a lot of L&D patients with other health issues because of my tele background. Not to mention, there have been several personal, familial, and friend health issues that I had knowledge about because of my time in telemetry. I was able to provide a lot of insight and comfort to my family members because of this.

Here are some routes that are known to work for getting a New Grad job:

Preceptorship

Clinicals or Precepting on a particular floor as a nursing student. While you are being precepted on a floor, you could be offered a position by the manager before you graduate. If this is in a hospital and is for a medical floor or other, you should probably take it. You might not get another offer for months.

Work in Hospital as Ancillary Personnel

Working as a CNA, Tech, Transporter, Unit Secretary or other personnel on a hospital floor before or while in school, while waiting to pass NCLEX, and then getting priority in the new grad program for that floor or neighboring floor. They might not be able to explicitly promise they will hire you, but most likely, they will if you are a good employee. Focus on connection building and be a person that others talk about positively. Make your job dreams known to co-workers (i.e., nurses) and the manager once you've built the rapport. They may not be able to create a position for you, but ideally, they will think of you if an opportunity arises.

Applying

Apply for a job, interview, and get hired. You may apply for many, many, many jobs before being invited to interview. Again, HR gets hundreds of applications for New Grad programs, so a lot of getting called to interview is based on some factors out of your control. But, the more programs you apply to, the more likely you are to get called to interview.

Important Tip: It's a very good idea to start answering your incoming phone calls once you start applying, especially local numbers. Just in case it's HR calling to set up an interview. And make sure your phone has space to receive voicemails. If you do get a voicemail, call back immediately. They might not hold an interview spot for you. Definitely do not play hard to get.

I was told by one of the unit secretaries in my department that she once went down a list to set up new grad interviews for our nurse manager, and when some of her calls went to voicemail, most of the mailboxes were full, and she couldn't even leave a message. She skipped over those people because she only had so many interview slots. Can you imagine missing out on a New Grad position in L&D because your voicemail box was full? And even if you see the missed call and call the hospital back 99% of the time, your caller ID won't show a direct number, just the general hospital number.

Hiring Events

Hiring events are worth checking out. This is a nerve-racking route but can pay off. If the flyer says Experienced RNs only, no new grads considered, know you might not get anywhere. I went to such an event, and I was told politely to leave. It was mortifying. You will find these events by subscribing to New Grad FB groups but also getting on LinkedIn and following every single hospital in the area that you are willing to work. They will post hiring events and New Grad programs. In going to a hiring event, you should be prepared to interview (tips for interviews below), and you should show up looking professional like you would to an interview.

Calling HR

Making a phone call to HR won't hurt. But even an experienced RN calling about a position, especially at a hospital most people want to work at, will likely get very rote answers, "all of our job opportunities are listed on our website," or "if we are interested in moving forward with your application, we will contact you." Essentially brushing you off.

Some additional action items to work on:

- Set up a Linkedin profile with professional picture
- Follow all of the local hospitals and beyond on LinkedIn or other professional sites.
- Clean up or private your social media accounts
- Set up a professional email address if yours sounds too casual
- List of jobs sites to check daily

Author's Note:

Years ago, after applying for every single new grad program in Southern and Northern California for several months, I saw a post on a New Grad Facebook group for a hiring event at a local hospital for RNs. In very fine print, at the bottom of the flier, it stated that a few new grads would be considered. I hadn't received a response from ANY of my efforts and applications submitted, and I was desperate. I decided that if they were gonna hire a new grad at this event, it was going to be me. The hiring event started at 9 am. I got there at 6 am, and I was second in line. I came with a friend, so we were able to take bathroom breaks and fix our hair. More and more people amassed behind us as the minutes rolled by. Suffced to say, my friend and I were hired, and when we walked out of there at almost noon, there was a snake of applicants 250+ deep. The only thing that was different between those people and us was that we showed up earlier. I want to say they hired about 15 new grads that day, all of whom I recognized from the front of the line.

Showing up to an HR department in person without an appointment

Again, you may be given a polite "go away." The exception to this was when I worked for a hospital while waiting to take NCLEX. I went to HR with my uniform and hospital badge and asked if they would tell me when the RN new grad application was opening. I was told they weren't allowed to tell me exact days, but it was usually the second week in June. So in that scenario, you may get some assistance.

Resume and Cover Letter

It's a good idea to have a resume and cover letter ready to go early in your last semester of nursing school. If anyone asks for your resume in a hospital or a new grad application opens, you'll be ready to tailor it for that role and send it off in minutes. You can find resources for resumes and cover letters at nursehelpdesk.com.

CHAPTER TEN

INTERVIEWS

Congrats! You've somehow convinced someone to interview you. Don't slack now. It's not in the bag. Here are some interview tips. The following might sound like overdoing it but you've come this far, why not put in a little extra effort to land yourself a job?

Preparation:

Do a test drive of how to get to the hospital, where to park, where you walk in, etc. Being familiar with your surroundings ahead of time can greatly reduce your nerves.

If it's a video interview, set up your camera ahead of time where you will want it. Have something set up to take notes. I recommend doing a practice interview with someone actually on your screen. If you are not used to this, your eyes will likely go all over the place, and you could be thrown off. I bombed a Facetime interview as an experienced RN by not practicing this.

Before my interviews I've practiced sample questions with a friend, and she coached me on how to answer things in a better way and to sound more professional. These weren't always the exact questions I was asked, but it did help me get in the mode of thinking on my feet. Also, we are not used to selling ourselves while also sounding humble and it's hard to do this off the cuff. Definitely practice! Sample interview questions are listed a little later in this chapter.

Before your interview try to not get into any deep convos that could result in an argument with a significant other, family member, or friend prior to an interview. Have the time leading up to the interview be low stress.

Should you bring a portfolio or resume to the interview? I never had a portfolio, but I know some schools have their students make them. I made resume packets that had my resume on top with letters of rec stapled behind. I brought 5 copies with me to each interview. I can't say whether this helped me or not, but I do think that my first RN job interview expected them; better to have them than not. I have heard interviewers dislike resumes on white paper because it hurts their eyes...I printed mine on light grey resume paper, cream would work too.

Clothing

Somehow, with some superficial and subtle signs, you need to show the interviewers that you:

- Are a professional
- Take safety very serious
- Are more likely to succeed than fail on their floor
- Are confident but not arrogant
- Exude customer service
- Have some concept of how to be an RN technically
- Have some knowledge of the hospital and respect it and would be honored to work there
- It's a lot to convey before even answering a question. How do you communicate this while saying nothing? The answer is...wear a suit.

I initially thought that a suit was ridiculous since, for the actual job, you will be wearing something very close to the feeling of pajamas. But, it is strongly recommended that you invest in a very professional interview outfit; it doesn't have to be expensive or even that stylish. Every nurse manager I have ever been interviewed by was dressed very professionally. A suit can show that you very seriously want the job. Get a suit or minimally a black/dark blazer that fits and black pants and a nice shirt to go under it with a nice pair of flats or shoes. This ensemble remains in your closet as your "nurse interview outfit" that you always have. I bought mine over 6 years ago and have gone to it for each interview. Doesn't have to be fancy. My blazer is from TJ Maxx, but it's never failed me. I have seen some male RN's wear ties.

Be very clean, freshly showered, styled hair, make it look like you put in the effort. I always blow-dried my hair and put it in a high, slightly curled ponytail. But do what will look good for you. Just think professional.

Fingernails clean, trimmed. Nail polish seems to be fine if you prefer. Imagine that they base their hiring decision on how well you care for yourself.

Leave your phone in the car or totally turned off. You can get a briefcase type thing from an office supply store for the interview, and it holds all of your resumes, etc. Bring this instead of a purse. It looks professional.

Again, you do not have to spend a lot of money to look professional. You are not going for a fashion job, so don't sweat too much about being super stylish or buying expensive clothes.

Ok, remember how you should prep for a test and NCLEX? Same story here. Lay out everything you will need the night before, everything ready to go, eat a good meal, time your fluid intake so you won't have to pee mid-interview, etc.

Upon Early Arrival

Always arrive early to your interview but not to the actual interview room. Arrive at the parking structure early, or somewhere else you can wait very close by, cafeteria, etc. I'd usually give myself at least double the time it takes to get there at the minimum, meaning if my interview was a 30-minute drive away, I'd leave an hour before the interview but probably closer to 1.5 hours before just in case there is traffic, etc. Then you will not be rushed. When you arrive, you can use the restroom and appear collected and cool. Show up exactly on time for the interview, up to 5 minutes early is also acceptable. Even a minute late is unacceptable.

Be nice to everyone you encounter on hospital property. The valet, the security people, the charge nurse who was in scrubs that showed me to the interview area for one job turned out to be in my interview. If you are rude to the valet, maybe your potential future co-worker is wheeling out a discharge and notices you. They could impact your future with a single report to the nurse hiring manager.

If you are seated waiting for your interviewer, do not be on your phone. Just don't. When someone comes to greet you, stand up and shake their hand, make eye contact, smile. "Nice to meet you." Follow them and answer their questions, "Yes, I found parking easily, thank you," "Yes, the weather IS beautiful today." Common sense, pleasant manners, and light conversation.

Panel Interview

RN interviews can happen in a couple of different ways, but commonly it's a panel interview.

You will be taken into some sort of conference room or office.

The setup can be in different ways. You could all be at a conference table, you could be seated in a chair facing three-four people, there are a variety of setups. Be prepared for anything.

The panel could be comprised of several managers, or a manager, a charge nurse, and another RN as a peer or some other setup. Usually between three and four people. I have found these interviews pretty intimidating, and getting through them is a rush.

When you walk in, usually everyone that's part of the panel will be there already waiting for you. I would say hello and introduce myself with a handshake to each person there to interview me. "Hi, I'm [name]," and smile. You can offer your resume packets to each panel person. I would hover near my obvious seat but wait to be told to sit.

Usually, the interviewer will pick up on what you are doing and invite you to sit.

There will likely be some pleasantries, and the panel will give you an introduction to who you are meeting with and how they plan to conduct the interview. Usually, each interviewer has a packet that has all of the questions, and they write feedback about how you answer. Try not to stare at these, meaning, do not attempt to see what they are writing. Pretend not to notice. Typically, each person takes a turn asking you a question. They often are the ones you speak to (with eye contact, please) when you answer that question while the others take notes but make eye contact with everyone when answering.

Your overall attitude should be to focus on listening to exactly what the question is and then focus on responding in an articulate, intelligent yet concise way. Let them get the entire question out and let it sink in. It's ok if you need to take a beat to formulate a response. Ideally, you will answer each question with a brief story or example that answers the question in an interesting way. This is why you should practice answering questions you don't expect and work out your answers ahead of time (more on that below). Check out the STAR method for tips on answering questions.

Some interviewers are nice and kind, some do their best to be intimidating. Try to exude confidence. You will receive minimal feedback on your answers. They will likely acknowledge you after every answer, but you probably won't know if you are doing well or not.

Panel Interview with Fellow Applicants

Some hospitals employ a particularly brutal technique where you are brought into a panel interview with several other applicants. In some instances, it will be a round-robin of questions, and you are answering in front of everyone. Or you will be asked to briefly interview your seatmate and then present to the panel why you should hire them. You may or may not be told this will be how it's done ahead of time, so just be prepared. Even while others are talking, look engaged, interested, and look at the person who is talking.

Interview Question Prep

I practiced sample questions with a friend, and she coached me with feedback to come up with better answers. These prep questions were not the exact questions I was asked, but they did help me get in the mode of thinking on my feet. There are websites with practice interview questions and below are some that I have been asked many times some with samples of how I answered or tips for answering these yourself.

There is a super common first question that I think can get messed up:

"Tell us about yourself."

When they ask you this, realize that they are not asking about you personally, they are asking about you professionally.

Sample answer: "Well, I just graduated from the RN program at Pasadena City College and just passed my NCLEX. I currently work as an LVN in an OB/GYN clinic. I'm seeking a position in telemetry. I love this hospital and got such great care here for stitches on my hand several years ago. I am hoping to join a team I can be with for a long time.

You would not say, "Well, I'm 27. I was born in LA, raised in San Diego, went to school for RN in my mid-twenties, met my husband at a 90's dance party, and now we live in Pasadena."

Practice a response that sums up your professional experience and why you are there today interviewing.

"What are your Greatest Strengths"

Sample answer:

I think empathy is one of my strengths. "I excel at anticipating patient's needs, and I can envision easily what would make their day or experience with me better." Then I would give an example of an instance when you did this. Or...

"I also have a strong sense of urgency. I am pretty good at spotting and handling things that need my attention and action right away and prioritizing what needs to be addressed first. I feel that I learned this as a server in a very fast-paced restaurant years ago. I know serving isn't the same as nursing, but there are some corollaries that I think will really help me."

Other questions I've been asked :

"What are your greatest weaknesses?"

"Tell us about a work conflict and how you handled it" I think that they want to see how you took action to solve the problem. How did you go out of your way to handle the issue so it didn't escalate to someone else having to solve it?

I gave an example about a time two doctors from my office both needed me to help them with procedures that were both scheduled later that day at the same time and that neither were willing for me to not assist them. I solved it by getting one doc to agree to go an hour later and calling the patient and getting their agreement to come in later.

"Tell us about a time you went out of your way for a patient"

"Tell us what you know about the hospital and why you would like to work here"

First, I would read their mission statement ahead of time. Also, find something specific to discuss about the floor and the great work they do or that your family/friend was well taken care of there, or that you had a very positive clinical experience and liked the teamwork. You can try to get more specific for the department if you can. A teaching hospital, Magnet Status, County Hospital, Patient Population are all topics you can hit as to why you want to work at a specific hospital and unit. E.g., I saw that one specific hospital I was interviewing for in L & D had a very low C/S rate, and I talked in the interview about how impressive that was.

Basically, come up with something other than just needing a job or convenience to where you live.

"Describe a failure and how you overcame it"

This one is challenging because you don't want to say anything that makes you look like you dropped the ball or were unsafe. I told my story about getting less than an ideal grade in a science prereq because of my dad's illness and him being on hospice during that semester (true story) and that this could have been an end to my nursing career, but I made it happen by repeating the science class and persevering until I made it.

"Describe a time when you had difficulty with a co-worker and how upon reflection, you would have handled it differently"

I used an example of a fellow student from my last semester who tried to ghost during clinicals or was on his phone all the time. I said I should have tried to be more willing to include him in tasks or in the skills labs.

They are looking for your ability to handle conflict on your own.

"How have you dealt with an angry or upset patient?"

I went with how I handled an upset patient, but in my example, I made sure it was clear that the patient was not upset with me.

"Name the 5R's" (Medication rights)

"What are your future career goals?"

Once I said was that I was looking to be part of a hospital family that I could remain in for my entire career. They really seemed to like that.

"Do you have future plans to move/relocate?"

I kept this brief and said I loved the area and wanted to stick around forever. If you are applying to a hospital far away from your home, I would say you are willing and able to relocate for the job. You can decide definitively after your offer but don't give them a reason to not offer you a job.

"Describe how you organize your day"

"How are you with handling a hectic work-place?" With examples.

You can find many more sample questions searching sites and forums and at nursehelpdesk.com. Aim for practicing 20 or more questions in random order with another person can help you a lot to be able to think on your feet in an interview.

Following up after the Interview

It's a good idea to send a follow-up email soon after the interview that says thank you. Usually, one of the managers will give you a business card. Worst case, you can send it to the recruiter or person who set up your interview, and hopefully, they will forward it for you. I would do it by the end of the day. Alternatively, you could write a thank you note if you have some way to get it to them that day. But it's my personal opinion that it's better to send a thank you while you are fresh in their minds so by the end of the day however you can.

Sample:

Dear Ms. Henry,

Thank you for taking the time to meet with me this afternoon. I am very excited for the opportunity to be considered to work in your department. As I mentioned, it has been a dream of mine to work in ICU since I saw my uncle brought back to life by the nurses there. It would be such an honor to work for you.

Again, thanks for your time and consideration.

Best Regards,

Your Name

phone/email

Your note should be short, sweet, praising her/his team. If you can tie in a special moment you had in the interview, great. But keep it to a few sentences. Also, always include your number and email, so people do not have to search for it if they need to get ahold of you quickly.

Bombing an interview

It stings when you find out, for whatever reason, a manager doesn't want you on their team. The best thing to do is get right back out there and keep applying, try to learn from the interview and what you can do better. Try to keep in mind that "rejection is protection" in some instances. Don't dwell on it too much, and just keep at it until you are hired. Usually, it will make sense later why something you wanted so bad didn't work out. But the patience and persistence to get to that point can be challenging.

The worst interview I ever had was over the phone. It was a facetime interview, and while I was prepared to question wise, but I didn't practice on the phone, so my eyes were looking all over the place, and from there, my answers felt like a mess. I also just felt that for whatever reason, the nurse manager and I weren't jiving, and everything I said wasn't well received. But what really nailed my coffin shut was when I asked two very specific questions, which I should have saved for after my offer letter was issued. The position was for 24 hours a week, and I asked if there was ever an opportunity to pick up more hours. The manager didn't like this. The second question was how long the transition from night to day shift was, and she really seemed annoyed at this. I also think she didn't understand my first question, and so I talked over her to rephrase my question, cutting her off. Big mistake. I did my best to be upbeat, but I knew as soon as I hung up the phone that I wasn't going to be offered the job.

Offer Letters

Congrats on nailing your interview and getting an offer. Here are some tips on what to know or consider before accepting that offer. These are also things to consider if you are juggling multiple offers.

- What is the length of orientation program?
- What is the pay?
- Is there an expectation or contract for how long you should stay on the floor/department you are hired in to? Penalties for leaving before that?
- What are the benefits?
- Is there a nurse union?

- Even though you are desperate for a job, these are very important points to consider and understand before you accept any position.

Life Events and New Jobs:

Let's say you have received an offer letter and are about to sign it. However, in two months, your sister is getting married, and you are Maid of Honor. You need a three-day weekend off minimally. This is the time to get it agreed upon in writing that you will have those days off. Email HR or your nurse manager and very politely write something like this:

Dear HR/Hiring Manager,

I was so excited to receive my offer letter today. Thank you so much for this opportunity, I cannot wait to start.

I have a small schedule issue I wanted to discuss. My sister is getting married the weekend of October 4-7. I am Maid of Honor, and I am hoping I can be blocked off from working those days. I am willing to work ANY other days or any schedule every other week to accommodate this, and I do not have any other requests for days off. The job is my #1 priority, but I promised to be there for my sister.

Please let me know if this will be possible. Thank you for your time and consideration.

Best Regards,

Name

Every time I have done this, it is approved, but of course, this is not a guarantee that your manager will agree. And getting it approved ahead of time causes a lot less stress for you going to your manager after they have already made your schedule. Do this via email to get it in writing.

Further Reading:

I highly recommend *Your Last Nursing Class: How to Land Your First Nursing Job: The Ultimate Guide to Landing Your First Nursing Job...and Your Next!* by Beth Hawkes. This nurse is an expert on this topic, and her book is extremely helpful.

CHAPTER ELEVEN

YOU'RE HIRED- ORIENTING AS AN RN

After you've signed your offer letter, you'll get your start date for orientation. Depending on the job, you might have some time for in-class like orientation or a mix of orientation and precepting. New Grad programs vary in length. From my start date to being on my own was 12 weeks, and I was hired into a telemetry unit. My friend who started in Med Surg got 9 weeks, and folks I've worked with in L & D got 6 months, so it really depends on your hospital, department, and program.

You will be on the floor a lot, and it will be very challenging. You will be assigned one or more preceptors, and you will follow their schedule. Some weeks you may have one or more days of classes, but a lot of the program will be on the floor.

Helpful Tips for Preceptees:

Everything about the etiquette of clinicals applies here. Be on time, be prepared, have proper supplies (pens, stethoscope, etc.), help the CNAs and other nurses when you can, learn everything. Here though, the stakes are way higher because they are going to throw you into the pool and watch you sink or swim. They might also set you up in scenarios where you will definitely sink, and actual patient outcomes will be on you, and they'll come in only at the last moment. Because they want you to learn. This is the real world, and this separates the new RNs that will make it and the ones that won't. But know that most make it.

Your preceptors may or may not be training you against their will. Either way, they are watching your every move and have the power to influence having you dismissed from the program. As they start to trust you more and more, they will back off little by little until you are doing everything on your own. They will be checking your work and hopefully building you up, not tearing you down.

Preceptor Gratitude

I wish I had done this sooner and more often in school, but once I was an RN for a while and switched departments and then hospitals, I realized how much effort preceptors were giving me for nothing in return. I started giving each person who precepted me for a day a $5 coffee card. If I knew I'd be with them for a few shifts, I'd give them more, plus candy or chocolate or snacks. I didn't make a big deal out of it, "Just to say thanks for helping me today." My preceptor in L & D, who spent a long time with me, got a larger gift card and other gifts.

It's such a simple gesture, totally worth the money. It shows the nurses that their time and effort are valued. It will go a long way in getting help and advice from these nurses in the future, and overall just giving some gratitude when I was seriously interrupting their day and making a lot more work for them. If you cannot afford this do not feel obligated, it's not required.

Codes & Rapid Response

Try to go to every code you can to learn how to be helpful and what the nurses do. You won't really learn until it's your patient, but any insight will build on your knowledge.

On your first day, you should memorize how to call a rapid response or a CODE.

Important Phone Number Card

Collect all of the important numbers you will need to get your job done, some to start with:

- Charge nurse:
- Workroom for MDs if there is one:
- Alert Team/Rapid Response:
- CODE team:
- Resource Nurse:
- Pharmacy:
- Lab:
- Radiology:
- Room service:
- Social Worker:
- EKG:
- IT/Maintenance (password resets, broken patient TVs, call lights, etc)
- Housekeeping:
- Resident's phone numbers:
- Ask your preceptor for the best numbers to have handy

You will memorize these eventually, but for now, you should have a cheat sheet of need-to-know numbers. Ideally, make the number small enough and laminated so it can hang behind your badge. While you are at it, buy a mini pair of trauma shears, and depending on your patient population, hang it from your badge or keep it near your labeled stethoscope. I use my scissors multiple times a day.

As a nurse you are the go to problem solver for your patients, all day long you are solving little and big problems. Having all of the numbers that help you get problems handled saves you a lot of time.

Preceptors and Orientee Etiquette

I have been lucky in that the majority of my preceptors have been very kind to me and put in a lot of time and thought into making me into the nurse I am today. They did this without additional compensation and I will be forever grateful.

I have also had a few people orient/precept me that clearly did not want to. I often took this personally and let it ruin my day, week, etc. I have realized now that 99% of the negative interactions (and there have only been a few in all of my years of nursing) I have had with preceptors have been because they simply didn't want to be precepting anyone, not me specifically. Maybe they were burnt out on orienting, or they just didn't want to be doing it but couldn't say no. Or maybe they are having a bad day, weren't feeling well, etc.

Years later, I have been guilty some days of being a subpar preceptor. I have failed more than a few days at being the best nurse for some students/orientees. If you are reading this, I apologize for not giving you a better experience.

The problem with preceptors getting burned out is that new nurses are made and shaped by other nurses with more experience. It's vital that this system doesn't break down. Extra support and compensation should be given to those who precept so we can make better (new) nurses.

Keep in mind that there will be days in your career when you work with strangers, people that aren't your good friends, or even people you like. You have to learn how to work with people who aren't outwardly friendly to you and sometimes you have to earn the nurse's friendliness. This isn't necessarily fair but often how it is. Your best bet is to focus on the work, work as hard as you can, accept constructive criticism and feedback and try to get better each shift. If someone says something about how you are working and it doesn't resonate with you, then acknowledge them and move on, you don't have to take what everyone says to heart just because they have more experience.

I have noticed that those who assimilate well into new floors generally work super hard and try to do over and above as a newbie, taking the hard assignments without complaining, helping other nurses without prompting, and not dumping work on others or the next shift.

Floor nursing is 24-hour care. Meaning, if you couldn't get something done on your shift, it's reasonable to think that you could pass this to the next shift. Beware that there is a fine line between something you could have gotten done and didn't and something that just isn't feasible to get done. You'll learn quickly after giving report to on coming nurses what is acceptable to pass on and what isn't. Some nurses are very attuned and sensitive to ANY extra work that they perceive is not their responsibility or could have feasibly been done by you during your shift.

Example: a patient's IV goes bad at 0600 when you flushed it to start an IV antibiotic and your shift ends at 0700. You don't try to start a new IV and 0700 rolls around. This is not an acceptable thing to pass on unless you tried multiple times, and no one else was around because everyone was running a code. Still, it's unideal to not have a working IV for your next shift and to have an antibiotic administration delayed. Another example: Patient needs an xray during your shift, you follow up with radiology at 0600, shift ends at 0700 and the xray tech says that it won't happen until 0800. This is something that it is out of your hands and would be more acceptable to endorse to the next shift.

Ideally, when you are on your own, you will have nothing outstanding for the next shift that you could have gotten done for that patient or you can prove sincerely that you were working so hard you ran out of time. This, and repeatedly giving it your all each day will simultaneously make you a better new nurse and will help you gain the respect of your colleagues.

CHAPTER TWELVE

GETTING THROUGH THE FIRST YEAR

There is little chance that you will be a competent RN out of the gate. Even years into this career, some new scenario comes my way, and I struggle to handle it. I learn from my fellow nurses every day in the way they explain something or go about a nursing task or handling an emergency. I ask for help and advice often. Ideally, you will have go-to people in your department that you can ask. Your biggest resources are (hopefully) the people that precepted you and the charge nurse, depending on your floor. You will learn quickly who is kind and willing to assist. On your first day solo, you might even have an assigned nurse to give you a little extra help; if not, the charge is likely looking out for you especially.

You may find yourself guilty of asking for more help and advice than others and will probably hit annoying status with some nurses more than once. You should try to pay this forward whenever you can by showing up for them. Bring snacks! Or throw in a few extra $ into the collection for pizza or a baby shower collection or bring more than soda to the potluck. Take over other patients while their primary nurse runs a code, or help move a laboring patient with an epidural whose baby is having a deceleration. Don't wait to be asked. Even when you are brand new, showing up for your teammates and helping when you can go a long way. Once you get your footing, you should consider that you have some responsibility to all of the patients on your floor, and you should always be willing to help. Your priority is to your assignment but always try to be on top of your patient's needs so your free time can be uti-lized helping or giving that little extra.

Your patient assignment is priority number one, but learning to prioritize and learning what is most important at that moment is a skill you will hone. For example, if you are helping the CNA take your patient to the bathroom and you hear a code overhead, you would get the CNA to help the patient back to bed and go help in the code, or minimally watch the other code participant's patients. It would be pretty lame if, after the code, your teammates found out you were hiding in a patient's bathroom. Another example would be if you have a critically low blood sugar and your patient is symptomatic, it would not be appropriate to leave that patient and go to the code. It would be vital to handle your patient's low blood sugar immediately (per provider's orders), so the floor doesn't have another rapid response or code to deal with. Makes sense? They are a million examples of judgment calls in how to prioritize, and these come with experience.

Doctors

No matter the culture of your hospital, interacting with new to you doctors/providers can be intimidating. I think you'll find that once you work with them long enough, carry out their orders, and are on top of things with their patients, they will warm up to you. I always try to address a doctor either on the phone or in-person the first time I see them with a Good morning, Good afternoon, or Good evening or similar. Practice your SBAR outside of work, and you will get better at it. Say thank you, follow up as needed politely if you don't hear back from them. Be professional always initially, not too casual, and then as the months roll on and they trust you, they will likely become more friendly, follow their lead.

I have found in teaching hospitals that usually the attending physicians are more patient with new nurses and the residents are more receptive, but not always. It depends on the culture.

Getting it Together

It is very common to fear and dread going to work. Most nurses I know felt this way as new grads.

When I started, I was a mess. I came home after my third shift on my own, and I was more upset than I had been for a very long time. I was sure that I was a failure, that my decision to become a nurse was the worst of my life. To say I was struggling through that first week was an understatement. I was totally in my head, so overwhelmed and rushed all shift. I had never experienced that type of overwhelm, and I had no escape. I recall going one of the days without peeing, taking a sip of water, or eating. It wasn't a good look.

It wasn't until I picked myself up and figured out how to get my act organized. I had so many tasks, and I didn't batch them well, so I was drowning. I came back the next week with my act together, my own custom brain (a piece of paper that tells you the needed info about each patient), my atti-tude adjusted "I'm the only one that can get me through this." and while the shift was bumpy, I did it better than the week before. Each shift, I got better, and you will, too.

Batch working for Nurses aka Time Management

One of the most important things to practice as a new grad is learning how to batch your work and tasks together. This means doing as many tasks as possible while you are in a patient's room and having everything you need so you are not going in and out constantly.

Starting an IV? Ensure you have all of the supplies you need, check to see if your patient has any labs ordered today that you can draw now with the IV start (if allowed at your hospital), grab the IV meds that the patient needs once it's placed and the antibiotics that are due in half an hour and grab the tubing for the IV, like that. Having everything that you could need for that patient they will need for the next hour or two to hopefully cover yourself and care for the patient while you are in that room.

I try to never go into a room empty-handed unless there's absolutely nothing left to bring in. I scan a room the first time I am in there to bring all the supplies I'll need for the day. Water, linens, baby blankets, check that the warmer is working, delivery supplies, check cabinets, etc. I set it all up when I assume care of a patient. Leaving my at-tention open to more important things.

Giving all the meds that I safely can at once and grouping tasks is huge in time management success. If a patient wants a PRN med, I look at the other options for PRN meds or other meds around that time and offer those to them to get it done. Grouping tasks and batch working are so so important.

For example, if I am getting a labor patient up after a delivery for the first time, I am also bring-ing her pain meds, I am going to put a new pad and underwear on her, take out her epidural catheter from her back, do orthostatic BPs, ambulate to bathroom, further clean her up and then after bathroom into a wheelchair to be transferred to postpartum. Before getting her up, I would make sure I had pericare supplies and meds in the bathroom and a wheelchair. I would have all of her possessions ready to go on a cart, and some-one on standby to push it, the baby wrapped up and ready to roll. I would add a lot of time if I split up any of these tasks into 2-3 trips to the room or didn't have all of my supplies.

Especially when you have 2-6 patients, depend-ing on your acuity and ratio, you would be better off doing as many things as you can for a patient while you are in the room, so you don't have to go back into that room for a while. Not to mention if a patient is trying to rest and you are in there every 15 minutes, they are going to get annoyed, especially if night shift. If you are ping-ponging every few minutes between rooms, you will drown.

You'll have to come up with your own system and brain to get you through those first shifts. Re-flect each week on what worked and what didn't and tweak your brain or patient info sheets ac-cordingly. I now just write some notes down on an index card for each patient, mostly to give to a nurse who might cover me for lunch. A lot of nurses I know don't write anything down at all.

Night Shift Success Tips

The majority of new grad positions are night shift. This is often because day shift is the most wanted by nurses, and an open day shift position is given to someone with more seniority.

There are definite advantages when starting on nights. It's generally less hectic; there are fewer doctors, less to no management, often amazing teamwork, fewer procedures to get patients ready for. The disadvantage is that you are tired most of the time. Night shift = Easier work-life, harder personal life. Day shift = harder work-life, easier personal life.

There are a ton of resources out there for night shift success. You will have the best outcomes if you try what other nurses suggest and see what works for you. I was most successful when I switched my entire life to a night shift schedule. On non-work nights, I would stay up until around 5 am and sleep until 1 pm. I might even take a nap before work. After night shift, I would be asleep by 8am and wake up at 4 pm, and go back to work, but if I was off, then I would then be up for the next 13-14 hours. It was worth it to me because it was the specialty I really wanted, L & D, and still being a relatively new nurse in a new specialty, I didn't want to be foggy, and my life could accommodate this (i.e., no kids). After having a child, when I work night shift, the key is getting enough sleep whenever I can. If you cannot sleep during the day, get a good night's sleep (at night) and then try to have a low-key day and take a nap before work. These are just a couple of options, and nurses are very open with their recommendations on FB forums and elsewhere. Search and you should find some suggestions of additional sleep schedules that you can try.

It's often not hard to stay up at night because you are moving all the time. The problem often is sleeping during the day. Expect the first few weeks to be kinda rough. Don't plan a ton of stuff during the days so you can prioritize sleep.

Products that help daytime sleep are blackout curtains (make your room as dark as possible) and some kind of eye shield, white noise maker, fan, and or a/c in warmer months to keep the room cool. Signs for the front door not to disturb you during the day or deactivate the doorbell. Earplugs, if you can deal with them; if it's really loud in the rest of my house, I might use headphones with white noise. Ideally, your phone is off.

I have felt the best on night shift when I eliminated sugar from my diet, but that's a real challenge because there is always sugar and candy at the nurse's station. I also feel my best on night shift when I exercise.

Prepare for feeling like crap until you adjust and do your best to get as much quality sleep, food, etc., so you can do your job well enough to keep it.

Closer to your Dream Job

After you have gotten around a year of experience, you might start to notice different areas/departments of the hospital that look interesting. Some options may include:

OR, PACU, Cath Lab, ED/ER, L&D, Postpartum, NICU/ICN, PEDS, and ICU

To find these opportunities, you can stalk your career website at work, go to HR and say what department and inquire about upcoming openings, be friendly with the other department staff that you interact with. You usually have a greater chance of getting a position in the hospital vs. outside candidates and in a hospital that you have a track record with. They might give you a chance and be more willing to train you in another specialty. You may hurt your current department's feelings, but hopefully, you gave them a year plus of your time, and they can't really fault you for wanting to grow in your knowledge. I wouldn't spread the info around in your current department that you are looking, better to announce it after you have accepted an offer, given notice to the nurse manager, and coordinated a transfer or resignation.

Second Job Interview

Everything about interviewing that is listed above applies, but this time, they may ask you more questions of what they would expect an experienced RN to know and possible department specific questions, so do your homework. Practice questions, wear a suit (minimally no scrubs) and avoid your current department if possible, so you don't get flustered by your co-workers asking what you are doing.

Continue pursuing the specialties you are interested in. Know many more doors will be open after that first year of experience. Put your head down, do good work and you'll get through your first year.

Further Reading:

I will recommend Beth Hawkes's again with her book, *First-Year Nurse: Advice on Working with Doctors, Prioritizing Care, and Time Management, For More In-depth Information on Succeed-ing Your First Year.*

First-Year Nurse: Wisdom, Warnings, and What I Wish I'd Known My First 100 Days on the Job by Barbara Arnoldussen

First Admission: A Handbook to New Grad Nursing by Jaison Chahwala

CLOSING

This text is meant to be an overview and guide taking you from considering the idea of a nursing career through your first job as an RN. We want you to be successful and want you to like this very unique profession.

I am happy to be able to share what I have learned at each stage of becoming a nurse. I hope it is useful and makes your road less bumpy.

I often remark that it was a very good decision for me to become a nurse. It was also a very good decision to pursue a specialty I love. There can be a lot of drama in this profession, fielding human emotion, enduring and being witness to human suffering. But there is a lot of respect and pride in the work and a lot of value in it. You ultimately have a job where you help people all day long. I don't regret it for a moment. I am happy to have you join our ranks. Best of luck to you. If you feel like you need more content on this topic, check out the further reading suggestions and follow along at nursehelpdesk.com for additional recommendations, tips and tricks as they come in.

Please reach out with your questions and feedback at nursehelpdesk.com.

Index

CPSIA information can be obtained
at www.ICGtesting.com
Printed in the USA
LVHW021431220422
716973LV00005B/506